STARTUP

Riko Radojcic

Published by Open Books

Interior design by Siva Ram Maganti

Cover images © ZinetroN istockphoto.com/g/ZinetroN

ISBN-13: 978-1948598552

OCTOBER, 2020

SAFE HAVEN

Here and now, I feel safe. This might be due to the effect that this place has on me more than the reality of my situation. Hiding in this old house, with its thick stone walls, double windows and wooden shutters, I feel secure as a mouse in its den.

Outside, I can hear the rhythmic sound of the waves lapping against the stony shoreline, some twenty feet from my window, and I can discern the sea, the mountains and the night sky, all blending into blackness along the Bay of Kotor.

And inside my head, I can also hear the now distant echoes of excited children—the sounds of my cousins and myself romping through my grandparents' seaside home. But that was more than half a century ago, so far away both in time and experience.

By way of introduction, my name is Andrija, but my Anglo friends, as well as my colleagues and neighbors, find the Serbian name hard to pronounce (it's that 'j' toward the end that always confuses) so they have long ago changed it to Andrew. By now I am quite used to it, or perhaps I am now truly more of an Andrew than an Andrija.

I am originally from what used to be Yugoslavia, but my compatriots managed to screw up that nation, and I was lucky enough to get out before the worst of the bloody disintegration. I was truly fortunate and after getting my EE degree at the University of Belgrade, I stumbled into a scholarship that funded my graduate studies in America. And I have lived there ever since, other than visits to the Montenegro coastline every couple of years to catch up with family.

And if neither Andrew nor Andrija works for you, then call me Professor. Everybody does, because I formerly taught at one of the top engineering schools in the world. But that seems like another lifetime, even though I left academia only a few years ago.

CIRCA 2010:
THE ACADEMIC

Good Old Days

Yes, I was a professor, tenured at a university that many of us believed to be equal or better than the famous Ivy League schools. Holding the coveted Alfred S. Harris endowed chair since 2001—an amazing achievement, if I say so myself, for an academic who at the time had not yet turned forty and with what then seemed like sufficient funding to pursue leading edge research in my chosen field: semiconductor technology. I had a state-of-the-art research lab, which at its zenith was staffed by half a dozen permanent technicians, a couple of associate professors, two or three visiting researchers, up to eight Ph.D students, a handful of MSc grunts, and a number of operators and administrators.

Yes, I was flying high back then. I could happily hand off most of the boring teaching chores to my TAs and concentrate on research. And my team was churning out some excellent work. We were publishing dozens of papers each year that routinely won awards and recognition at many industry events and conferences. Our grant applications were frequently funded by DARPA, or SRC, or NSF or even by various private foundations or corporate programs. Attracting talent was not an issue. The best and brightest were vying to join my team.

Back then I was like a rock star in the business, and invitations for keynote talks, review papers, contributions or simply introductions to various technical books were often extended. I could happily turn down all sorts of speaking engagements, even the private corporate invitations that offered those obscene, but so very tempting, honorarium fees—$10,000 plus expenses for a lecture and a two-hour-long round-table chat—evidently a small price to pay for an opportunity to nourish the egos of a few corporate bigwigs who enjoyed grandstanding in front of a famous professor.

Yes, it looked like the millennium had brought good things for us, and the sky was the limit.

And not just professionally...

Bev and I had met back in the '90s in one of those combined interdepartmental undergrad classes—something like 'Science, Technology and Society.' I got involved with the course because it was trendy, and an easy way of earning an extra teaching credit. A feather in a cap for a newbie, especially because such courses were shunned by the more senior professors who did not have to worry about burnishing up their teaching rep. I thought that teaching science to non-scientists would be easy and would not require much prep work—something that I could easily do off-the-cuff. But as fate would have it, the class held something much more significant than teaching credits. The moment I walked into the first lecture, I noticed her, and everything changed. It was not just the deep azure eyes that were such a contrast to her jet-black hair, or the tight jeans that showed off all her beautiful curves, or... It was the dimples in her cheeks that seemed to amplify the sparkle in her eyes whenever she smiled. And the tiny furrows between her knitted eyebrows whenever she raised a question. And the insidious acuteness of the questions she would raise.

I must admit, with all the brilliance of hindsight, it was lust at first sight—certainly so for me. Ethics be damned!

"But, Professor Krstic, *why*...?"

Sounding awkward and tongue-tied, I tried to focus on the question rather than on her.

"Please explain..." With dimples framing a most enchanting smile, her eyes dared me to impress her.

So I had to be stellar in that class, just to keep up with her questions. I mean, how does one explain magnetism or electricity to a non-engineer without sounding stupid or condescending?

But as we got to know each other, the relationship deepened, we fell in love, moved in together, and...well...lived happily ever after. A couple of years later we married. We bought and renovated a perfect house in a good neighborhood. Sum-mer breaks in Europe—often in Montenegro where we con-gregated with my family. Winter or spring breaks in Mexico. Fall weekends camping in New England... A few years later Lara came, our wonderful daughter, which of course changed everything. All for the good, though. Diapers, pre-school, play dates, kindergarten, school. We settled into a family routine of two professional careers and a kid and looked forward to the continued bliss of middle-class existence in modern America.

―――――――

But then Moore's Law caught up with me. Of course, Moore's Law is not a law of physics but is rather a historical trend that states that the number of transistors in an integrated circuit doubles every couple of years. What became obvious with the brilliance of hindsight was that in order to enable that dou-bling, the equipment used to make the chips was necessarily becoming more complex. Exponentially so! And the price of that equipment was exploding, too. Certainly, the technological miracles that this equipment enabled suggested that some of the basic laws of physics did not apply anymore. Like printing features many times smaller than the wavelength of light used to define them!

Yes, the late aughts were a time when not only the research labs, but also small, medium, and even full-sized factories—fabs in the lingo—were priced out of relevance, to be replaced by mega fabs: the only ones who could afford the state-of-the-art equipment, which ran into tens of millions of dollars. These Mega-Fabs cost a few billion dollars; an investment that could be amortized only by run volumes of the order of tens of thou-sands of wafer-starts per month. Literally, acres of silicon! Vol-umes that could be supported only by standard and commodi-ty products—like general purpose processors or memories. Or that had to be smeared across many IC products from multiple customers—like with the offshore foundries. Tough times even for the industry to fund a team with a dedicated research lab—let alone R&D institutions or academia.

I was discovering that in order to maintain the relevance of my lab, I was spending an increasing amount of time on the road seeking funding for ever newer and more expensive equipment. I stopped being a technologist and instead became a beggar. Not to mention that I stopped being a father and a husband and instead became a road warrior. And to make things worse—adding insult to injury, so to speak—the people whose butts I needed to kiss to get the necessary funding seemed to be getting progressively younger. Maybe it was I who was growing older, but the men that I needed to impress seemed to me to be looking more and more like my students. I found it a bit humiliating to be begging for money from self-important brats who were not smart enough—or humble enough—to know just how little they actually knew. Not something I expected to be doing at my age, having achieved the status for which I'd worked so hard...

Of course I tried to adjust to the changing realities and shifted the focus of my group to the more specialized analog, RF, and even MEMS devices. And then stooped to scraping the proverbial barrel with some of the technologies used for advanced packaging. We shifted toward niches in technology that were the domain of smaller, less sexy, and far poorer sectors of the industry while trying to remain a big fish, albeit in a smaller pond.

But it was all to no avail.

Students—the *job whores* that they are—adjusted their focus toward arenas that were more likely to get (and keep) them employed. Other departments in my prestigious university—the Computer Science, System Architecture and Chip Design Technology ones—were attracting the cream of the crop. And consequently, the work of my team was becoming ordinary—certainly less stellar. Over time, the only good talent that I could attract increasingly came from abroad: the obsequious Indians; the hairy Persians; the mumbling Chinese; the pushy Koreans. All seemingly blessed with rich daddies and driving shiny BMWs. While I, their brilliant prof, was hiding behind the façade of an absent minded and indifferent academic who could not be bothered to upgrade his clapped-out old Toyota.

The degradation—this slow erosion of our significance—was,

of course, quite gradual: so much so that at the time it was almost imperceptible. I certainly was not aware of it on a day-to-day basis. Maybe just on those rare occasions when I ignored the in-my-face issue and took the time to ponder the bigger picture. Like on those long summer weekends when Bev and Lara might have been away somewhere, leaving the house empty. On such occasions I would sometimes allow myself a couple of glasses of bourbon, rather than working late on some paper, or on reviewing the student intake for the coming year, or writing a grant application, or tending to whatever bureaucratic chore-de-jour may have been the pressing issue. Or during some long transoceanic flight when my body was sufficiently confused by jetlag that I could not go to sleep, and just could not face opening my laptop to catch up on all the email traffic with the students, sponsors, colleagues, conference organizers, or whoever else needed an urgent response. Not that these occasions of deep reflection—some might call them navel-gazing sessions—made much difference. I could—and did—shift my attention onto topics that I thought were important. But it made little difference. The industry trends were dominated by factors far larger than me and my lab. I feared that I was just flotsam riding upon an oceanic wave. Of course, most of the time I was successful in pushing those realizations to the back of my mind and carried on being—or perhaps pretending to be—the brilliant professor who had so much to contribute to the field of semiconductor technology.

I first met Aram around that time—around 2012, a few years ahead of the nadir point in the arc of my career as a hot shot academic researcher. He claimed that he had been in one of my undergraduate classes the previous year, but I had not noticed him then. I became aware of him as an individual—as opposed to a faceless student—when he signed up for one of my graduate level courses, because of his name, Aram Khachaturian. Like the composer—that veritable genius who had written several pieces of modern classical music that happened to be among my favorites. When I asked him about it—if he was related to the composer, he explained, "Khachaturian is a very common Armenian surname. It was derived from a trade—like Smith in

English." He further elaborated that Khachaturian was based on the Armenian word for 'cross' and therefore implied that some ancestor of his had probably been a priest or maybe a crusader.

Interesting and notable, I thought, since my own last name—Krstić—has an identical meaning in Serbian. We had a good laugh about that: we were practically twins.

He also stood out in the class, The Physics of Solid-State Semiconductors—one of my most popular ones. Not so much due to the brilliance of his work, which was pretty good, but because he was actually paying attention to the lectures I was giving. Taking notes, asking questions, and actually getting it. Not like most of his fellow classmates with their noses buried in their laptops or phones and only peripherally aware of my existence. I don't know if the growing malaise of my career at that time was warping my perception, or if the quality of the students—even those at the graduate level—had actually deteriorated, but I did find their indifference quite disrespectful.

Sometime later Aram came to my office and asked about working in my lab. He was looking into doing graduate work on Artificial Intelligence—a topic that has been around for a while but that has all of the sudden become *sexy*, another of those new solutions— like GPS or Uber or whatever—which were not new in principle but have been resuscitated by the technological advances enabled by Moore's Law. Artificial Intelligence methods were defined back in the '50s and '60s, but the necessary training data sets and cheap compute power became practicable only in the 2010s; hence, the resurgent interest. Regardless, it was a good topic for research. And I told him so.

He said that he did not want his doctoral work to be just 'pencil pushing' (his choice of words) and that he hoped to do something hands-on. Something more than just writing code and doing computer modeling and simulations, which was the bread and butter of the design groups. He wanted to focus on an aspect of AI design and architecture that could be demonstrated using the capabilities of my labs. He wanted to build and/or test suitable representative vehicles. He wanted to do something 'real' (again his choice of words) not abstract. This was of course music to my ears, and I readily agreed to support, and even to co-sponsor, his graduate work.

Since then I have talked with Aram more or less every day, but back then the interactions with him became the highlight of my days. He was bright and stimulating, eager but not foolish, intelligent, and hardworking—a joy to have as a student and a colleague.

During his graduate work years, we grew close—more so than the usual professor-student relationship. Nothing inappropriate, of course. No, Aram and I just got to the point where we could drop some of the formality in our relationship, and on those nights when we were both working late, we could even have a beer and a bite together. More like friends and equals. I liked him.

It was during one such late night 'beer-and-burger' outing that he first floated his idea of starting a company based on our research work. He'd talked before about not wanting to work for someone else, but that was vague; just talk. Not an unusual feeling amongst graduate students who viewed the prospect of a career in the corporate world with a sense of foreboding, no doubt amplified by fear of the unknown, their liberal idealism, and the trendy disdain for 'the man'.

But for Aram it seemed to be more than just an aversion to becoming another cog in a corporate machine. In his case, it had more to do with family lore, which dictated that working for someone other than oneself was for losers. Apparently, most of his ancestors—going back to their pre-genocide Armenian roots in the Ottoman Empire—had been self-employed businessmen. "I come from a family of independent merchants, so a startup company seems like a natural fit for me. Genetic predisposition, I guess." He shrugged.

I suspected that he felt it was the only way that he would gain the respect of his traditionalist Armenian family. I got an impression that they were biased toward the pursuit of wealth rather than acquisition of knowledge. He had a couple of older brothers and a fairly strong 'big-daddy' kind of father—each of whom were involved in the family business, which provided building supplies and associated hardware throughout the state. According to Aram, the three of them thought that he was wasting his time by going to graduate school, and they were not shy about telling him so. In fact, it had apparently become a sort of family joke: lazy, bookish Aram who shied away from 'real' work.

And I suppose his scrawny, nerdy looks did not help. He was quite skinny—almost skeletal—and full of nervous energy, constantly scurrying about and twitching his stick-like arms.

To me, personally—at least to my face—Aram's family was always polite; cordial and respectful. Aram occasionally invited me to various Armenian community celebrations: Orthodox Christmas and Easter, Armenian Genocide Day, Independence Day, and the like. So I had a chance to meet his family on a number of occasions. I suspect that being Serbian, and Christian Orthodox, helped, as their rites and traditions, foods and the ways in which they behaved, were not altogether alien to me. So I was not a complete outsider. But neither did they treat me as an insider. They were obviously a tight family who shared their true impressions only amongst themselves.

Nevertheless, no matter how much Aram denied it, I believe that he felt that a startup was the only way he would impress his family and justify his years at the university. "Why would we *not* do a startup, Professor?" he demanded. "I'm serious: we'd have to be stupid or blind or both to ignore such an opportunity. We could turn our combined knowledge and know-how into some real money. AI is the up-and-coming thing. I know it. You know it. And we have an AI technology solution like none other." Enthusiastic and eager, he always got intense about making money.

"Well," I tempered, "because there is much more to it than just saying that you want to do it. You need a good product idea. You need to do serious work to define a business plan. You need to get the seed money by selling the idea to very smart, and very skeptical, people who hate parting with their dough. And then you need to actually develop the best product on the market. And you need to have enough luck along the way to not fail like the nine out of ten startups that end up going under, which, by the way, are staffed by people equally smart and equally motivated as you!"

CIRCA 2016:
THE SEED ROUND

GERM OF THE IDEA

"Well, Professor? What did you think?" Aram asked, plopping down in the chair on the other side of my desk.

But that was just the pretext. Over the last few years as he was doing his grad work, I had gotten to know him. Usually, when he came to my office like that, he followed up a specific question—the pretext for the conversation—with the real subject that he wanted to explore and discuss and debate and argue and... I learned that he was not exactly a man of few words.

"The more I think about it the more I am convinced that it is now or never," he carried on before I had a chance to react. "In a few years a set of AI standards will emerge, and when that happens the business becomes a race to the lowest margin. Real money is made before that—if you can get your technology to shape the standard. I just finished some business books about that. Look at Qualcomm and the phone market, or Intel and the laptop and server markets. The window of opportunity for serious money in AI is tight."

Aram was trying to engage me in yet another conversation about his startup idea—again and for the nth time. The initial question was aimed at my review of the latest revision of a slide presentation for his startup—sort of like a skeleton of a business plan. But the broader topic that was of real interest to him— this time obviously about the norms that the industry practiced with adoption of standards—could take hours to explore.

At that particular point in time I was determined not to be drawn into a lengthy debate with him. I was busy, and besides, it was getting old. I'm sure that my exasperation—not to mention my absent staring out of the window—was not lost on him.

And it seemed that the closer he was to completing his doctoral work, the more frantic he became about the startup, and the more often he initiated these discussions. Quite naturally, I suppose, since he did not have anything planned for after graduation. Most of his contemporaries had a job lined up by that time, and some were already employed, choosing to do the wrap-up chores for their theses in their spare time. Some of the luckier ones—mostly the rich foreigners—had plans for trekking around the world or pursuing some other dream.

Aram had none of that. By conscious and determined omission he'd made sure that he had no options. He did not apply for work anywhere, or participate in job fairs, or do anything of the kind. I don't think that he even prepared a resume. It was almost as if he was purposely avoiding anything where there was even a remote chance of someone offering him a job. The only alternatives that were left open for him were to either go work for the family firm or to pursue his startup. I am sure that he perceived the former as a total failure and that he would rather have all his teeth pulled than join the family company; thereby forcing himself to be wholeheartedly committed to the latter option—the startup.

But turning that option into reality needed work. It was not like he stuck his head in the sand and did nothing. In fact, he completed the paperwork, spent a princely sum of $125 to create a Limited Partnership company—an LLC—on paper. Nor was it that he was ignorant of the practicalities of running a company. Partnership charter, roles and responsibilities, bank accounts, payroll, place of doing business, accounting and legal framework—he had made plans for all that. He had it in his blood, he boasted, having grown up watching his grandfather and father run a business.

No, it was mostly that high tech was an expensive and complex enterprise fueled by specialized knowledge—nothing like running a hardware supply company. And to kick off a technology startup he needed to define and communicate real vision and to plan everything two to three years ahead, all in order to attract the right talent. And to do that, he needed to get startup money. And for that he needed help…

"Look, Aram, I agree with you." I decided to focus this time on the specific topic of his presentation, and to avoid the more general open-ended discussion. "I do think that AI is the hot topic. Industry buzz is all about AI and the Internet of Things. So the VCs are more likely to listen, which is why there are already dozens of AI startups. And possibly many more still in stealth mode..."

He nodded vigorously and mumbled something about now being the moment.

"And I agree with some of the mega trends that you highlight in your presentation," I carried on. "Your claim that there is a class of applications where the bulk of the AI processing would have to be executed locally makes a lot of sense to me—because the bandwidth and latency requirements for communications with the Cloud would be prohibitive. Not to mention that it is the best way of dealing with many of the security and privacy concerns. And yes, I agree that for these applications the AI chipset would follow the economics of a consumer device—like the phones, rather than that of the enterprise infrastructure—like the servers. And I agree that your architecture with an analog neural network processor, and with pre-defined chiplets that are integrated at the package level to match a specific application, is probably the right cost-performance trade-off. All true..." I trailed off.

He did have a slide deck intended to describe the core idea behind his startup, and the fundamental technical solution that he was proposing. Work-in-Progress, I thought.

His opening argument presented the global picture and emphasized that the real value of the myriad of devices—the IoT—generating massive amounts of data was in the data itself, and that AI was necessary to parse that into something useful. Otherwise we would drown in data, and trying to do anything manually would be hopeless. Paralyses-by-analyses. That was a good point, I thought, something that anyone paying attention would get—especially if some eye-catching statistics were added. Maybe the projected number of electronic devices in a regular home or in a car, followed by the consequent number of GBytes of data that these would generate, or something along those lines...

He then had a few slides that were derived from the side of his thesis work that focused on design. These showed that most typical AI architectures could be mapped into a chipset that used a set of common denominator building blocks, including the CPU and the Neural Network Processor, DRAM, Flash, FPGA, etc. It turned out that there were good theoretical reasons why regardless of the AI end application, such as speech or image recognition, or playing strategic games, or running a smart home, or whatever, the common denominator building blocks were necessarily quite similar. But used in different ratios and interconnected a bit differently, depending on specific system architecture.

There were also a couple of slides that leveraged the technology side of his thesis project, and that explained the theoretical reasons why these building blocks necessarily had to be manufactured in different technologies. These implied that even if it could be realized in practice, implementing a complete AI system on a single chip—the so-called System on Chip or SoC—would be a sub-optimal compromise solution. And he had slides that explained why building an AI system out of multiple off-the-shelf ICs would end up in a solution whose cost, size, power and performance characteristics would all align to limit its applicability. He added a slide that emphasized the point about AI computation at the Edge, rather than in the Cloud, and the associated performance and security benefits based on the last discussion that we had on the topic.

The core idea behind his startup was that for higher volume applications, such as the ones that relied on AI processing at the Edge, the optimum cost-performance would be achieved if the building blocks were pre-designed and manufactured separately in suitable specialized technologies. They could then be integrated into a multi-chip module at the package level using the so-called 2.5D and 3D integration technologies. That way a solution could be optimized to meet the requirements of a specific class of applications without having to redesign everything. Sort of a Lego block approach. The alternative would be to design a custom SoC solution for each class of AI applications, which would necessarily have a cost structure that could be supported only by a cloud-based implementation.

Honestly, I felt that these slides still needed work—partially because no one, or very few people, would have adequate expertise in all the areas that he leveraged to make a case for his startup: AI architecture, chip design, manufacturing and packaging technologies, costs and the way economies of scale worked in our industry... He needed to dumb it down and make it less technical. That was always the hardest part for engineers.

Furthermore, all the other things that an investor would need to see in a Business Plan were missing. The market analyses and the Total Available Market, the competitive analyses and the Serviceable Available Market, and especially the target business structure... How was he planning to make money, when, and from whom? He needed to define the basic product. And who were his target clients? End consumers, or other businesses in the supply chain? He needed to define the business model: License fees for software or IP, or per part charges for IC hardware, or service fees for implementation engineering, or even advertising... Oftentimes it was the innovation on the business side that made a successful startup. For example, the real innovation that made Google the behemoth that it became was the idea to make the application software free, and sell users' data to advertisers. It had nothing to do with the technology behind its search algorithms. Also, for hardware companies, amortizing of the humongous up-front development costs had to be addressed... And he definitely needed the numbers—credible investment profile and profit and loss numbers that even the savvy VCs would believe...

"None of that changes all the other facts that we talked about," I persisted, to remind him of the realities. "This is not close to a complete and credible Business Plan. A good idea alone does not make a Business Plan. You need a lot more, Aram. The business model, the market, and the numbers—especially the numbers! Time to money, target investments, headcounts, expected P&L, risks and competition... I would like to help you, but I am slammed. You will just have to find someone else." I found the situation somewhat awkward.

On one hand, I thought that Aram was a bit naïve about

what it took to start and then run a successful high-tech company (as opposed to running a building supplies company), and I felt an obligation to bring him down to earth. It seemed like the right thing to do. Over the years I'd served as an adviser for several startups, so in addition to the general knowledge about the industry that came naturally with experience and maturity, I also had some second-hand knowledge on the topic, which I felt I should share.

On the other hand, he was enthusiastic and positive—and probably right! I did believe that he had a viable idea and that there was an opportunity. And I liked him. So encouraging and helping him also seemed like the right thing to do.

But such a balancing act needed attention—and time. And time was something I was short of right then. Between the usual university chores that tended to be particularly pressing at the start of the academic year, and the cut-throat competition for funds for research projects that seemed to have dried up since the Great Recession, and the routine publish-or-perish activities associated with the conference circuit, I was slammed.

"I know, Professor, you are busy," Aram responded, his dark eyes radiating disappointment. "But I need you. There is no one else who would be as good as you. To be honest, I don't think that my startup would be viable without you, without your network, or your reputation..." He let that hang in the air, perhaps trying to guilt me into joining his venture. He had doggedly refused to hear my 'no.'

During one of our many discussions he even suggested that I take a sabbatical and get involved on a full-time basis. And I actually did consider it. I even talked it over with Bev, my 'She-Who-Must-Be-Obeyed.' But Bev dismissed it out of hand and wondered if I might be going through a midlife crisis or something. Perhaps she was right. Always the sensible one, she reminded me that our plan was for a sabbatical in Europe the following year, and that she was looking forward to it and arranging for a leave of absence from her own job. And that the university rule was that sabbaticals had to be arranged six to nine months ahead of time, and even when approved, they usually involved a cut in pay. Not something that we could afford right then, she reminded me, with Lara going off to college. Not to mention that taking time off to engage in some startup was not looked upon favorably, and usually did not play well in the cutthroat competition for grant money.

He then ventured tentatively, sort of like he was feeling his way, "What if I could find some seed money. What if I found an angel investor willing to float us a few hundred K?" He looked serious. This was not Aram simply daydreaming.

"I would applaud that, of course!" I decided to play my positive and supportive role. "Maybe with the funding you could finally get the right people to partner with you." I then added my usual disclaimers: "But that cannot possibly be me. C'mon, Aram, I'm not going to leave my position at the U. No matter how good an idea your startup might be... Not at this stage of my career, or at this stage of my life... You need to find someone else." We had talked about all this before.

"Then will you at least meet my angel? Help me talk him into funding us?" he persisted.

I easily understood that this was not just his usual enthusiasm talking—a characteristic that allowed him to mix wishful thinking with facts in equal measures. I suppose that this optimism, based on some kind of Steve Jobs-like reality distortion field, is a necessary ingredient for an entrepreneur. The ninety-nine percent of us who are not wealthy and who have to worry about mundane things like making a living are inhibited—maybe bogged down—by what most would say is realism and would give up before we started. The remaining one percent among us who actually do take the risks to start companies must surely be endowed with an unusually large dose of the ability to believe in their own wishful thinking. And Aram certainly had it. But looking closely at him, I concluded that this time his question was not founded in wishful thinking. He had something—someone—in mind.

I hesitated. "Who is this angel of yours?"

"You will have to come to see... The meeting is Thursday at eight o'clock, at the Armenian Nights restaurant; and I promise you, it will be interesting."

I had come to know that the easiest way to end a conversation with Aram—especially when it came to something that he was passionate about—was to agree with him. Otherwise, it either became a lengthy discussion or an exchange that had to be forcefully truncated. And I disliked abruptly terminating a conversation with him. It seemed like a rude and a cruel thing to do to someone as keen as he was. On those occasions when I did, he would skulk away with his proverbial tail between his legs, which always made me feel somewhat guilty.

Why not, I thought to myself? Good Armenian food, and Bev was so into her current project that she probably would not miss me anyway. Lara, even less so, being in that phase of life when any association with her dad was a bit of a pain.

"I know the place," I said. "I can walk there."

MEETING THE ANGEL

People I know had mentioned Armenian Nights as an exponent of genuine Caucasian cuisine, so I was excited to try it. But
at first glance it had the look and feel of a regular urban eatery.
It occupied a few rooms on the ground floor of a multistory
redbrick building typical of older East Coast cities away from
the glitzy steel-and-glass business centers and was like many
establishments that cater to neighborhood families in the evenings and serve the local business lunch crowd during the day.
The ethnic feel was conveyed by deep red walls decorated with
colorful, hand-woven rugs, a few rusty-looking sabers and anti-
quated muskets, a smattering of old photographs of fierce looking men sporting impressive mustaches, and a set of brass trays
hanging on the walls. And rather than using plain white linens,
the tables were draped in red, blue, and apricot striped table-
cloths meant to match the colors of the Armenian flag, which
was proudly displayed in the corner of the room. And the smells;
the unmistakable aromas of grilled meats, baked breads and pies,
and spicy stews marinated in saffron...

I spotted Aram waving at me and I made my way to one of
the corner booths.

"This is Professor Andrew Krstić," he introduced me to two
other men.

"Tigran Sakafian," one of them responded in a deep calm
voice, not sitting up or offering to shake hands but instead waving me to a seat across the table from him. I don't know if it was
just the sound of his name that subliminally suggested it, but
the moment we were introduced the mental image of a tiger
came to my mind. Or maybe it was his bearing and unhurried

movements that communicated confidence reminiscent of a top-of-the-food-chain predator.

His dark, round head with close cropped black hair, black eyes and prominent eyebrows complimented his medium build. I guessed his age to be about forty-five or fifty.

I must have been a few minutes late because the three men were already seated with drinks before them: Aram, Tigran, and another man whose name I missed when he was first introduced, but whom I now know as Stiglitz. But Tigran had that effect. Something about him seemed to suck all the oxygen in the room, and other people somehow faded into the background.

Tigran nodded and a waiter appeared to fill my glass from a bottle that was already opened. This was my first introduction to Armenian dessert wine, and its amber color surprised me. I learned that this was due to a special aging process that gave it a taste that was a bit like madeira but sweeter. Odd for a before dinner drink, I thought, yet somehow appropriate with the selection of cheeses served on a cutting board at the center of the table. Later I found out that this was one of Tigran's peculiarities: cheese, nuts and fortified wine before dinner.

Tigran then described how the Armenian wine making tradition was the oldest one in the world, that it used extended fermentation in large clay pots, and that it was all now on the UNESCO World Heritage list.

The introductory small talk then moved on to the usual discussion about my roots, and we compared notes on various traditions and customs that are shared between Armenia and Serbia. Even though they are more than 2,000 kilometers apart, we do have church, history and many cultural traits in common. Although, Tigran assured me, that since the Slavs have settled in that part of the world only since the eighth century, we were just transient newcomers—along with Turks, Huns, Tatars, and others. As opposed to the Armenians who seem to have roots in the region going back to 3,000 years BC. Altogether, either it was just the inflated myth of a small tribe, or a major gap in the general knowledge of most people, but Armenians seemed to have a very rich history going back to Mesopotamian times. He pointed out that Armenia was even mentioned in the Old

Testament since Noah's Ark came to rest on Mount Ararat, and that Armenia was the first country to formally adopt Christianity as a state religion. All factoids that I had heard before—seemingly achievements of which all Armenians were proud and readily shared in 'mixed company.' Tigran sounded very knowledgeable on the topic and used many superlatives. Oldest... Biggest... Tallest... Best...

He spoke with an accent—not softening the consonants or swapping 'g' for 'h', like the Russians tend to do, yet still somehow reminiscent of that part of the world. He used full and proper sentences, so typical of people speaking a language that they had learned through formal education as opposed to the usual idioms and conversational corruptions used by the natives and assimilated regular speakers. But it was clear that he was comfortable in English—not, as they say, fresh off the boat.

I do not know if they had pre-ordered before I arrived, or if Tigran was a known regular at the restaurant, but various types of food were served and empty plates were taken away with no overt orders that I could detect. The food was delicious.

Sometime after the *meze*, and as we switched to regular wine, Tigran cleared his throat and simply said, "So?" which must have been a signal that the preliminaries were finished and that he wished for the real meeting to begin.

Aram snapped to attention, produced a printout of his pitch, placed it in front of Tigran and started his presentation. He steadily worked through his slides, painstakingly defining the Artificial Intelligence technology. Tigran listened closely and occasionally nodded.

My sense was that this was missing the mark—after all, Tigran was not a VC or an industry insider who could readily follow Aram's slides. So after a few pages I interjected, "The big picture here is that this Artificial Intelligence—AI—is an essential element of the next renaissance; the next wave of change in society and how we live. Just as steam engines drove the first industrial revolution, and computers drove the second, AI will drive the third."

Tigran looked at me almost as if seeing me for the first time, and asked simply, "Why?"

"Well," I explained, "so-called futurologists—people with crystal balls who opine about the future—all seem to agree that our lives will continue to be shaped by more pervasive and ubiquitous electronics; the smart home appliances, smart robotics, smart cars, smart cities, smart everything... It is apparently an inevitable evolution of society driven by rising standards of living, shifting demographics, continued urbanization, climate change, and other factors—trends that are unlikely to change for the foreseeable future. And the consensus in the industry is that AI technology is essential for digesting all the data and for realizing that 'grand vision.' Just as the steam engine enabled the railways and the revolution in mass transportation, and as computers were essential to realizing the interconnected society of the internet era."

Tigran nodded and waved for Aram to carry on.

Aram did, but after a few more slides I again felt the need to intercede. Perhaps it was the wine and the food that conspired to loosen my tongue, but I felt compelled to elaborate. And so it went: Aram and I fell into a pattern. Like a tag team in wrestling, with Aram driving the key points and giving the technical details, and me adding the color and providing a simplified bigger picture.

Throughout the pitch, Tigran listened intently. I am not sure how much of it he understood, but he did not interrupt or ask questions. He just listened, occasionally sipping his wine or nibbling on something. But he was clearly alert and attentive. When we finally fell silent and Aram collected the printout, he simply said, "Thank you."

A long pregnant silence ensued, with Aram—and I guess me too—beginning to fidget nervously, looking for some hint of his opinion, or perhaps hoping for a question, so that we might further impress him with our brilliance. Something... Anything...

Tigran nodded at the waiter, and yet another bottle of wine was brought to the table, this time a deep, red claret. Tigran described it as an Areni Noir from the Vayots Dzor region. This, of course, meant absolutely nothing to me at the time, but with all the brilliance of hindsight I now know that it was something special. In truth, they could have been serving Ambrosia from

Mount Olympus and Aram and I would not have noticed. We were tense, on edge, nervously waiting for acknowledgement.

Finally, Tigran leaned forward and said, "In my experience people often don't say what they really think, or they dress things up to make them sound better. Perhaps they believe that this is more polite, or that it makes them seem wise. But I find that it often leads to misunderstandings. And sometimes misunderstandings result in bad endings..."

At the time I thought that he was perhaps enjoying stringing us along. But, again with the brilliance of hindsight, I now know that he was simply taking his time because that was his nature. In fact, knowing him the way I do now, I realize that it would have been presumptuous to assume that we mattered enough to influence his habitual approach.

"The technical points that you mentioned," he explained, "this Artificial Intelligence, the 'edge' versus the 'cloud,' package integration, and so on... They mean absolutely nothing to me. I am not educated, and I certainly do not know anything about electronics..."

Aram and I looked at each other not quite sure how to react. After carefully selecting a morsel of something and a sip of his wine, he continued.

"The only thing that I do know about technology is that there is a lot of talk about it. Even in Yerevan not a day goes by without some newspaper article mentioning technology. Maybe about some big western firm opening an office in Yerevan or forming some collaborative venture with the University or the government. With all that noise, it seems that putting some money into technology would be a wise investment...

"In fact," Tigran continued, "I have been advised—no, urged—to invest in certain technology joint ventures. But it seems to me that these enterprises are in Yerevan only to access cheap labor. And cheap labor, even if it is of the intellectual kind, is never a way to make good money. You always want to be the best, never the cheapest, particularly so when dealing in a new line of business. You must come in from the top—never from the bottom. So, if I am to invest in technology, I want to be at its source. Here, in America. From what I understand, this type of technology is mostly an American art. Not so well developed in Europe. Some progress in China, but there again, they are a source of cheap labor. Some in Korea and Japan, but in the end, they are probably minor players. No, the center is here. Therefore, I believe that America is the place to invest in this kind of technology. As they say, if you want to make real money in a casino, then you must play the main table."

After a pause he added, almost as an afterthought, "As it happens, I am diversifying my other businesses and branching out to America. Recently, I've needed to come here every two or three months. And when I do, I try to look at opportunities in technology." He trailed off, clearly implying that this was not the first meeting of this kind for him, and that investing in US hi-tech was a piece in his financial puzzle.

"I have no doubt that both of you know all about AI and silicon technology," he confirmed, "and that everything you say is true and correct. In fact, I confess, I have cheated. I had Stiglitz check you out."

He laughed when he saw our concern and went on to assure us, "Do not worry; nothing too invasive or personal. Just a few online searches and conversations with people who know of you… He assures me that you are genuine. And rare, which was another reason why I chose to meet with you.

"However," he continued after a pause, "I do know about people. And I know about business. And, let me tell you, technical knowledge is not enough. There are others who have similar knowledge." He paused there, taking a sip of wine.

He looked pointedly at Aram. "I believe that you, Aram, do have the drive to build a company. I believe that you would leave no stone unturned to make it succeed. I like that. To be successful you must have that kind of passion. So I would seriously consider investing in *you*, Aram, more so than in your technology. And not because you happen to be Armenian, although, as far as I am concerned, that does not hurt," he added with a smile. "Except people will not give you money, Aram… Because it is risky to invest in a fervent believer like you. Real businessmen do not invest in zealots.

"So, you need the professor here," he said, nodding at me.

"A source of wisdom, balance and credibility... People would be much more likely to give money to *you*, professor," he said, turning to me. "Your pedigree and knowledge, your reputation and bearing, and maybe your white beard, would make them feel more confident."

Before I had a chance to protest or to thank him, or to react in any way at all, he concluded, "So, I listened to your presentation—thank you again—and I believe that Stiglitz was right. Together, you two are...promising. Hence, I am prepared to consider investing in you gentlemen. But only under certain conditions."

He then proceeded to elaborate on those in the same deliberate way that he seemed to do everything. On the other hand, I am sure that Aram and I were probably sitting there like idiots with our mouths wide open as he listed his constraints.

"First," he began, "we will form an equal partnership: one third each." We were too surprised to protest, so he continued. "If you prefer, we can complete the paperwork to make it all legal, but contracts do not mean much to me. I will expect an old-fashioned agreement between honorable men. After all, there is no point going into business if we start out by not trusting each other. I cannot abide liars, and I admit that I can be quite vindictive with people who betray my trust. A handshake and a hand-on-heart oath is what I expect. First we agree, and then we do what we say we will do. No excuses and no exceptions."

He gave the impression that this was not the first time he'd entered into this kind of a situation, and that he knew what he was doing; whereas I, and I believe Aram, too, was too stunned to say anything.

After a pause, punctuated by a sip of wine, Tigran carried on. "Number two: in my experience these kinds of ventures work only if all the partners are equally committed. It is too early for us to talk about specific goals and milestones for this company, such as how much money it might generate, and in what time frame, because I understand that there are others trying to do something similar to what you describe, so a competitive environment exists. My experience is that in such circumstances it is the *commitment* of the people that determines who wins. Those who are willing to do anything to win, do win.

"So," he carried on, "I will expect that the three of us will commit to stay the course. We will commit to work together to surmount all problems, especially when things get hard. We commit to making the venture a success no matter what it takes. No plan B. No one walks away. That would be dishonorable and not much better than lying... So, Aram, I will expect you to commit your life to this enterprise. I believe that you already have, but I do want it to be clear. You will not have things in your life more important than the company—like a wife or family—until it is done. You will have no room in your heart for anything other than this venture."

To my surprise, Aram did not protest or even blink. In his place I would have resented someone limiting my personal choices, but Aram just sat there like a stone.

"You, professor," Tigran carried on, "will commit all of your time as well as your reputation, knowledge and judgment. You will have no other projects or concerns distracting you until we either succeed or agree to dissolve the partnership."

I wanted to protest that I had a job at the university, a family to feed, and so on, but Tigran cut me off. "Hear me out, Professor. These are my red lines, and I will commit money and influence— however much is needed to make our partnership succeed."

He stared steadily at me and Aram, took another sip of wine, and then continued, "Condition number three: we will be partners, but please let us not confuse that with being family. Outside this venture, we will stay out of each other's lives. Within the venture, we, each one of us, will have a role to play, and we shall trust each other enough not to second guess. How or why you make your technical decisions is not for me to question. And I will not. Similarly, you will not question my business decisions, and specifically, I need you to understand that you are not to question where the money that I invest comes from..."

He must have recognized the discomfort that this precipitated—at least in me—and added in a slightly lighter tone, "The reason I feel that I must bring this up is that I understand that there are some cultural differences between you Americans, and us Armenians—or for that matter, all of us who grew up in

Soviet Caucasus. Just like in America you do not question how much money a man makes, in our part of the world you never question where a man's money comes from. It is rude and dangerous because it may force one to either lie or betray other confidences."

Even at the time this concerned me. It sounded somehow threatening, and not something that I expected from an investor in tech development. But Tigran was not 'usual' in any way, so I held my tongue and waited for him to finish his list.

But apparently his conditions had been stated. "If these terms are acceptable to you, then we can talk about doing business."

We remained at that restaurant until two o'clock in the morning—three hours past their normal closing time. Empty, now totally quiet, and with the tables cleaned and all lights turned off except for the area around our booth. The staff, as if under some kind of psychic control, continued serving us. We finished with desserts that reminded me of the traditional Serbian sweets: baklava and a version of poppy seed rolls. I remember thinking at the time that in Serbia we always thought of those as Turkish desserts, but that they may have predated the Ottomans and come from Armenia, or Assyria or some other older descendent of the Mesopotamian culture.

Anyway, as the evening—or should I say the night—wore on, we gradually grew more comfortable, and reached the point where we could speak our minds openly and truthfully. Conversely, Tigran, the true orchestrator of everything that occurred that evening, was no doubt comfortable all along.

BIRTH OF THE COMPANY

That is how Mak'Ur AI, Inc. came to exist.

I know, odd name for a company, but these days, it seems that Silicon Valley has shed its old rules, and tech companies have been freed from having to include the usual 'MOS' or 'Tech' or 'Com' in their names. Aram also thought that the apostrophe in the name could be made into an interesting feature in the logo. We had quite a discussion about that. Funny how everybody seems to have strong opinions about superficial things like company names or logo designs. It seems that those witty Parkinson's Laws about the workings of an organization are all true. Something about the time spent on an issue being inversely proportional to its importance...

Anyway, Mak'ur apparently means 'clean' in Armenian—or at least in the version of Armenian that relies on the Roman alphabet rather than their own squiggles. It was a name suggested by Tigran. He mentioned it in passing at one of our meetings while expressing his wish that the company *be done in the American way*.

"By the book," he explained, as opposed to using any of the short cuts so popular in the Caucasian countries, apparently necessitated by the arcane ex-Soviet rules promoted by corrupt officials. Tigran wanted to see if it really was possible to do business without greasing any palms.

But the name stuck. First just as a placeholder, then we became used to it, and it is now the formal and official name of our company. Mak'Ur AI, Incorporated.

We—Tigran, Stiglitz, Aram and I—hashed out many of the issues, concerns and random details that came up, first that evening at the Armenian Nights restaurant, and then in all the subsequent meetings that we had, speaking our minds, openly and truthfully, like real partners.

I, of course, protested immediately that I was not a young man and that I had family obligations which kept me tied to my career with the university.

Tigran nodded and explained that he knew and understood this, and asked if doubling my pay—which would not be out of line with a CTO position in a commercial entity—would address my concerns. He indicated that he would be more than willing to fund that as proof of his own commitment to the partnership. He also assured me, in his steady baritone, that after the thirty plus years at the university I would still have a guaranteed pension, and that my leaving now would not affect that pension very much, and that after all, should anything go badly, which, of course, he reassured me would not happen as long as we all remained committed, then I, a famous professor, would have no trouble finding another university position. Or, he emphasized, should everything go to plan, then I could retire as a wealthy man.

At the time I had the passing thought that Stiglitz might have done his homework too well, and that Tigran knew much more about me and my finances than I was comfortable with him knowing. But other things loomed larger in my mind right then, so I just shelved the concern and said that I needed to think about it and talk it over with my wife.

He nodded and said that he would be in the US for another couple of weeks, and that we—both Aram and I—must take that time to think things through.

"Of course you must talk it over with your wife and family. And you must be sure. In your heart. I would not want to deal with you if you were not."

His perspective sounded reasonable. Also, I liked the thought of retiring as a celebrated entrepreneur and a wealthy man.

Yet, I was quite concerned about Tigran's requirement for a total do-or-die commitment—à la the commitment that Faust had made. Tigran laughed, clearly understanding the reference despite his claim of little education, and commented that this would therefore make him the devil.

He then explained that in Armenia we (meaning Americans) have a reputation of happily moving across the country to take a new position with another company just for a few extra dollars, and that therefore he wanted to hedge against the American habit of job hopping. He assured me that he was not expecting the kind of Armenian traditional loyalty where generations of people worked for the same master, and jokingly promised that Lara was free to work wherever she wished.

And he insisted that we all would maintain an attitude of reasonableness—that the partnership would accommodate someone being sick, or having a family crisis to deal with, or needing to retire, or whatever other human needs might arise.

While talking, he often made the sign of a cross in the typical Christian Orthodox way, and said 'God forbid' several times, presumably to ward off jinxing us by even mentioning such things. Evidently, Armenians, like most people from Eastern Europe, were quite superstitious.

Nevertheless, it all sounded reasonable to me, and I confess, I felt better.

Still, he insisted, he did not think that the partnership would work if the principals felt free to leave for greener pastures half-way through the development, or when things got hard, and mentioned how this could also get very messy with disputes over intellectual property rights, trade or other secrets, and so on. He repeated that this was a deal breaker for him and that it must be a one hundred percent commitment or nothing at all; and that going back on a commitment was, in his eyes, unforgivable.

I must admit that a part of me was very much attracted to the idea of a tightly bonded group that this insistence on commitment implied. It seemed unlike the environment at the university where my fellow academics acted as independent prima donnas seeking their own glory at best, and functioned as competitors at worst. This was more like *The Three Musketeers*: *"One for all and all for one!"*

In addition, I expressed my concern about not knowing, or even questioning, the source of the money. I explained that in this age of terrorism and drug cartels there were strict laws that required proof of provenance for certain financial transactions. Tigran shrugged, indicated that he was very familiar with those laws, and that Stiglitz would take care of it.

He then elaborated that since he himself was busy and had to spend the majority of his time in Armenia and Europe, he wanted to be a silent and unnamed partner, and wanted Stiglitz to assume his place in absentia. He suggested that Stiglitz take on a role of a CFO, as well as a co-founder, but assured us that he was not proposing to bring Stiglitz in as a fourth partner. Apparently, they already had some kind of an understanding between them as to how their interest in the company would be shared. He added that this arrangement would be far better for the company when reaching out to incremental investors since Stiglitz had an MBA, and as such, he would be a useful asset in developing the business plan, in addition to managing the finances of the enterprise and acting as the link to source funding. Stiglitz was to act as Tigran's avatar. In my mind, Tigran's response boiled down to asking us to leave all financial matters to Stiglitz. This did not really address my concern, but I assumed that they—Stiglitz and Tigran—knew what they were doing and may have felt that the financial arts were beyond an academic like me. And I had no wish to be a bean counter, and besides, it was his money...

In addition, in one of the subsequent meetings when we talked about the financing strategy, we agreed that Mak'Ur should follow the conventional arc and go for the usual Series A and B, and possibly even a Round C funding, prior to exiting, partially to raise the necessary money, but mostly to gain added credibility. Tigran indicated that whereas he was committed to bankroll the venture, he did not wish to tie down the billion dollars that it would take to launch an IC product, and that diversifying risks was always a good approach. Hence, bringing on additional investors would be beneficial as long as it did not mean losing control of the company.

The point about the extra credibility attained by bringing known VCs on board made perfect sense to me. In fact, I was a bit surprised—impressed even—that Tigran showed so much knowledge about standard Silicon Valley practices. He had clearly done his homework.

Aram was over the moon. His usual fidgeting amped up and he was almost quivering. I doubt that he slept a wink that night. Getting him to calm down and consider the situation objectively was quite a challenge. Of course, I pressed him to tell me where he'd found Tigran. "Armenian gossip mill," he explained. "I picked up a rumor about an oligarch from Yerevan that was looking for a technology investment. So I poked around and ended up contacting Stiglitz. And the rest is the glorious history to be!" he concluded with an ear to ear grin.

I tried to probe deeper, but that was pretty much the entire story as it presently stood. Aram did not have any specifics on Tigran other than that he was supposed to be one of the richest Armenian oligarchs. Wine and brandy trade, and apparently significant interests in several gold mines, according to Aram's local Armenian rumor mill. But, he indicated that he had a cousin who was dating a Russian-Armenian that only recently had moved to States, and that he would ask her to shake the rumor tree back in Yerevan.

"Apparently they're chatty yentas there," he said confidently. "Let's see what shakes out. But whatever we hear over the grapevine, I'm told that he's good for whatever money he promises."

That was somewhat reassuring. I mean, we were considering hitching our fortunes to Tigran's cart, and knew little to nothing about the man. Having someone check his background on his home turf sounded like a good idea.

Then I probed him about Stiglitz. Aram said that he'd done some homework on him too, and had managed to confirm that Stiglitz held an MBA from The University of Chicago Booth School of Business and a Bachelor's degree in Economics from Northwestern University. Just the reputation of those two institutions was somehow comforting to an academic like me. But other than the top line of his resume, Stiglitz seemed not to exist. He did not have a Facebook profile, was not on LinkedIn, and did not seem to have any kind of a footprint in any of the Social Media platforms that Aram checked. He was not the author of any published papers, or even a dissertation theses. No work history. Neither a Google search nor the Armenian rumor mill (normally a source of all sorts of real or imagined factoids about everything on the planet, especially involving conspiracy theories) turned up anything on Stiglitz.

"Who cares?" Aram declared. "What does it matter? The only thing that matters now is the money. So, let's wait a couple of weeks for our paychecks to show up, and then we'll know for sure. Why would anyone cough up the kind of money we're talking about if they were not serious?" Then, after a second or so, he added a sarcastic afterthought: "Unless, of course, they wanted to swindle us out of our share of the investment—the whopping zero dollars and zero cents that we are putting in!"

Of course he was referring to the agreements that we, the partners, had made: that Mak'Ur would be formally launched on November 3, starting with paychecks for the three founders: the CEO, Aram, the CTO, me, and the CFO, Stiglitz, and with a deposit of $100,000 'operating capital' and a line of credit good for another $200,000. To start with…

All this was subject to a final and binding handshake that Tigran had talked about, and scheduled for the day of his return to Yerevan, October 17. The time between then and November 3 was apparently all the time that would be needed for Stiglitz to complete the paperwork and formally create Mak'Ur AI, Inc., a C-Class Corporation, incorporated in the great state of Delaware.

At the time I questioned forming a C-Class Corporation. I was not an expert by any means, but my understanding was that this classification was meant for large entities, with onerous sets of rules and regulations that even companies with established accounting departments found daunting: quarterly board meetings, reports to SEC and IRS and shareholders, projections and forecasts, and God knows what else…

"Well," Tigran reassured us, "we will not be a publicly traded corporation at the outset, so all the shareholders are in this room. But why not form a C-Class Corporation now, rather than an LLC or an S-Class, just to save a few dollars. Why not set up a two-tier shareholding structure right up front to ensure that there will be no dilution of control as the company grows. Let us start the way we mean to evolve. We want Mak'Ur to grow into a C-Class Unicorn, so let's set it up that way from the start."

Again, he sounded like he knew more than I did and the principles that he was bringing up made sense to me.

In a subsequent private meeting with Aram—even as we were still trying to decipher and understand Tigran and Stiglitz—Aram pointed out that we would have plenty of opportunities to find out more about Stiglitz, and even Tigran, afterwards, and repeated his personal mantra, "Right now, all that matters is the money."

He agreed that the situation was a bit strange, and added that he too was curious about certain essentials—such as whether Stiglitz actually had a first name, since he always seemed to go only by Stiglitz.

I was quite wary, and expressed concerns that it seemed too good to be true. All the subliminal wisdom that I had, probably shaped by the Serbian lore with which I was programmed, called for caution. After all, even with the homework that Stiglitz may or may not have done on us, Tigran knew about us only a little bit more than we knew about him. What kind of a man would be willing to invest hundreds of thousands based on cursory information? Unless, of course, it was some kind of a scam... "There has to be a catch here, Aram," I fretted. I was genuinely worried.

Aram insisted that he could not conceive of one since Tigran was putting up all the money. "Right now all that matters is the money," he repeated. "If the money is there on November 3, then who cares about anything else?" he rationalized. "Maybe he knows more than he is letting on... Maybe he recognizes a good thing when he sees it... Maybe he has money to burn... Maybe we are just lucky... Maybe he is really our fairy godmother... Who cares why? All that matters is the money..."

I did not have a good response, especially not one that I could voice to Aram. It was clear that Tigran would be willing to fund Mak'Ur AI, Inc, only if I were to join. To him, it was a package deal. Aram was to be the unrelenting driver; I was to be the 'resident adult.' Both Aram and I had to commit. And I could not face Aram and tell him that I would pass on this unique and magnificent chance to fund his startup based on some unsubstantiated concern—a worry or a vague impression—that I could not even articulate. So I let it go. I did not like holding back, but at the same time I felt that there was no sense belaboring the point.

Making the Commitment

The last remaining barrier prior to committing—and prior to the 'handshake' that Tigran talked about—was to get Bev to come around. This was a big issue for me.

I rationalized to myself that if she—the ever-sensible one among us—was okay with it, then my misgivings were probably off the mark. In effect, that was outsourcing the final decision to her, but I had confidence in her judgment. Besides, she was the lawyer in the family.

I, myself, was torn. A part of me was afraid to leave the security of my university career. Another part of me was leery of Tigran and Stiglitz. Thirdly, there were the alarms and red flags that I was seeing. And a part of me was agog about the possibilities of a startup and the fame and fortune that this would bring. And lastly, I did not want to disappoint Aram. And, if it finally had to come to that—having to say 'no'—it would be easier for me if I could pin my refusal on Bev. "My wife won't let me," which would be much easier than, "I'm too scared to let go of my lifeline, and I think that there might be something fishy here."

I tried to manage that critical conversation with Bev the way I knew that she would. I mean, normally I am the impulsive one, and I stupidly tend to blurt out whatever comes to mind, sometimes—well, often—resulting in all sorts of misunderstandings, which then require backtracking and explaining that cost a lot more time and angst than it would have if I'd only planned it properly from the start. Not a good way to handle the life-changing decision that I was considering. On the other hand, when Bev had something serious that she wanted to talk about, she made sure that we carved out enough time with no interruptions. Depending on the topic, she also sometimes softened me up ahead of time. I am not sure if she knows that I am aware of this strategy of hers, but I must admit, I usually enjoy being softened up. Anyway, I decided to try to do it 'the Bev way' and arranged for a Sunday hike in the Ohiopyle State Park to be followed by lunch at the Aqueous Restaurant—both favorites of hers. We lucked out with the weather, and the fall colors were glorious. Good way to soften *her* up, I thought.

But a leopard can only change his spots so much—or however that saying goes—and I blurted it all out in the car on the drive to the state park.

She again reminded me of the plans that we already had in place, and again inquired—only half joking and eying me suspiciously—if this was some kind of a mid-life crisis.

I did not dwell on Tigran's commitment 'leash' and other things that worried me. It was not that I hid them from her—it was more that I glossed over them and instead emphasized the perfectly good arguments that Tigran had made, stressing the doubling of my salary and all the things that we could do with the extra cash, such as the car and house repairs that we'd agreed to postpone until Lara finished college. Not to mention—if successful—the opportunities for serious money a few years down the road, and the security which that would mean for Lara and for our retirement.

We then lapsed into an introspective silence, interrupted only by a series of terse fact-finding question and answer exchanges. That lasted for the rest of the drive and for most of our walk to the falls, the end point of our hike. Its setting was picture perfect with the rust and amber colors of the trees, the blue sky, the sound of the water burbling and birds celebrating, and the smells of the forest.

I then brought up the point that up until then I had not quite thought through myself—the emotional side. The fact that I felt that my career at the university was not going anywhere any more, and that I was pretty much stuck in the rut. And that all I had to look forward to was more of the same. Yes, it was safe and secure...and boring—so, so boring! That I feared that I was sliding into obsolescence and becoming one of the many irrelevant old academics droning on about subjects of little modern interest. That I felt like I was losing the respect of my peers—and maybe (probably) even my students. Sure, perhaps we could call it a midlife crisis—albeit at fifty-six I was supposed to be past that—but why not go for this startup as a kind of a last hurrah of my career? I explained that I feared that if I did not do it now, then I probably never would. And that I would possibly—maybe even probably—regret it down the road. And then I repeated the points about the money, the pension, and the probability of finding an alternative position should the venture fail. So, really, there was nothing to lose...

Bev listened. Bev understood and was understanding. Bev brought up the 'sensible' concerns, like medical insurance, the inevitable stress on my health, or on the health of our relationship—all valid concerns.

We talked about it more during the walk back to the car, then during the drive to the restaurant, and during the delectable meal that we had on the porch overlooking the golf course with that magnificent view of the mountains in the distance, then during coffee, and again during the drive home.

Finally—I think it was during coffee, or maybe in the car on the way back—she rendered her judgment. It might be just my preconceived perception of how lawyers think, but as always she gathered the relevant data, cross examined the principal witness, and prepared a balanced and thoughtful brief. Or maybe it was just a supportive partner rationally considering all options. Either way, God bless Bev.

She first stressed that she'd made a conscious choice when she married a poor university professor—making mock air quotes around 'poor' for emphases—and not some rich business executive, and that she was still very content with that decision. For her the financial argument was irrelevant. "But," she added, "I do understand that fame and wealth may be something that is important to you. Ultimately, it is *your* career. So if trying on the entrepreneur hat is what you want, then you should go for it. All the concerns about this Armenian financier of yours are neither here nor there. However you turn it, going down the path of a startup will involve risks. So what? What is the worst that can happen? Just tread carefully and don't do anything stupid."

She then turned to face me: "Look, as far as I am concerned, I do *not* want to spend my old age with a bitter old man filled with regrets and disappointment. I'm sure that the aches and pains that come with aging will make life hard enough without regrets. I will cheer you on whatever you decide to do—whether you choose to go for it, or to stay at the U. It's up to you. I'm your cheerleader either way."

I love that woman!

She then went on to explain that if the shoe was on the other foot, and it was she who wanted to change her job or her career, then she would expect the same support from me. Although we both knew that she—a passionate civil rights lawyer—was unlikely to change.

And it did not occur to either of us to talk about relocation, about time on the road, about 'offers that could not be refused,' about morality and ethics, or any of the other issues that I was to face. We both just assumed that the fundamental things—like who we were and where we lived—would not change.

Of course, had I thought about it more rationally, I would have realized that her response did not address any of my concerns, and that she'd passed the responsibility of the decision right back to me. But I took her response—her permission, her support—as a sign of approval, because in my core, I really did want to go on this adventure.

So we agreed. "Let's do it!"

The morning of Tigran's flight back to Yerevan, we, the three founding partners: Aram, Tigran plus Stiglitz, and me, met at a private country club that happened to be close to the airport. On that fateful day—a rainy and cold October morning—Aram and I drove there together. Our credentials were checked by the guard at the front gate, who had to make sure that we were on an approved guest list, and we had to sign in with the concierge in the lobby. The place stank of money.

The deal was sealed in an intimate dining room richly paneled in wood that gave the light that trickled through the lace curtains a soft and warm quality even on that gloomy day. Peaceful harp music played in the background. The waiters seemed to glide on air. The smug tranquility of the place was quite a contrast to the knot-in-the-belly that I was tamping down. We shook hands over a table cluttered with silver coffee pots, matching dainty creamers, tiny silver sugar spoons and plates filled with French pastries. The bond was sealed. And Mak'Ur AI Inc. was born.

The only remaining thing that I had to take care of was to write my letter of resignation.

I thought that would be hard, so I carved out an evening at home, poured myself a glass of bourbon, and locked myself in my study. But it turned out to be a lot easier than I'd thought it would be. After all the years I'd spent at the university—thirty years since my graduate days—all the highs and lows —a lifetime, really, I wrote the four lines that I knew would change everything.

CIRCA 2018:
SERIES A ROUND

Ramping Up

November 3 came and went; Mak'Ur AI, Inc. became a reality!

The money—our paychecks—arrived on schedule. And it kept coming every two weeks, like clockwork. This certainly helped to ease my anxieties—or at least pushed them into the background. Especially as our bank accounts showed numbers that made my eyes pop. Even months later I did a double take every time I looked at my pay stub just to reassure myself that the numbers were real. After years of working at the university with the fairly stagnant salary of an academic, the pay was gratifying, particularly so for the first quarter when I was still drawing a paycheck from the university. It was nice to finally have money to spare.

Funny how quickly we got used to spending some of it, too. It was not like Bev or I went crazy—not at all—but we did take care of things that we'd been deferring for years. We replaced my aging car—it was on its last legs—but I did not buy a flashy Porsche or a Beemer—just a regular boring VW. And we remodeled the kitchen after having talked about it for years. Those were discrete purchases that we would have had to take care of anyway. But I also noticed that our average expenses started creeping upward too—simple things like buying better wines, or dining at more expensive restaurants. We stayed at better hotels when we went somewhere for a weekend and we paid for better quality when buying shoes and clothes. I certainly felt more secure.

As per my commitment to my partners, I did submit my resignation. The first Monday after the official kickoff of Mak'Ur AI, Inc. marked the point of no return. The dean claimed that he was surprised; he thought that I would be the one to turn off the lights as the very last person to leave the department. I must admit I'd never liked him. I'd always had the impression that he considered himself to be above me. So, I confess, in some ways it was gratifying to quit. In the end, we negotiated a graceful transition period, and I agreed to carry some of my teaching load through the fall semester, as well as a half load during the winter semester. I also stayed on as an adviser to my counterpart who inherited my labs, and I agreed to carry on with some of the university chores—committees, advisory boards, reviews, and so on, for a couple of semesters. On the whole my departure was gradual, and we parted on good terms, which proved to be helpful when it came to licensing the IP.

Aram and Stiglitz, however, dove right in. Aram completed the remaining work for his PhD theses in a month rather than the three that I was expecting. After that he was virtually living at the office that Stiglitz had organized for us.

And Stiglitz had not only found nice office space in a kind of incubator business center, but also had tapped into some arcane-sounding stimulus fund that picked up the tab for virtually the entire rent.

We had a game plan. Aram and I—with full participation from Stiglitz—hashed out a strategy. We defined a three-pronged approach focused entirely on getting to Series-A funding and concentrated exclusively on the definition of the company. We were not going to be distracted by trying to develop an actual product or doing anything technical—not yet.

In my experience, the most common failure pattern with tech startups was diving into product development before fully understanding the market. I have seen it over the years; tracking the general high tech industry news, observing the startups that some of my grad students were involved with, or with companies that asked me to join their Technology Advisory Board. Engineers being engineers, we often tend to shy away from what we feel is sales and marketing 'fluff.' We like to retreat into our comfort zone and focus on developing a product. Because we know what we know, and therefore do not need to listen to the marketing types: people who we often disparage as 'pink shirt men' or 'guys with ties,' and almost look down on. In fact, I have seen techies who were proud of making that lethal mistake and even bragged that they were concentrating on the fundamental thing—the product—and not wasting time on marketing and business development superficialities. Often only to find out that they'd expended most of their resources on developing a *wrong* product. This meant that, if they had understanding backers, then they had to execute one of those 'pivots' that Silicon Valley is famous for and develop a totally new product? If they were lucky. Or, if they were more typical, it usually forced them to blow the rest of their resources on refining a failing product over and over again…until they went out of business.

No, we were not going to make that mistake. Not on my watch.

OBJECTIVE 1:
INTELLECTUAL PROPERTY

The most technical of the short-term company objectives was to secure a position with intellectual property. I felt that this was vital for the success of the company and thought that we should take care of it right away. Aram agreed wholeheartedly and we started by securing a license to all of the Artificial Intelligence IP that the University owned. As much as we would have liked to get some kind of preferred access to the IP that in fact we—mostly Aram and I—had created, the university had limited degrees of freedom when it came to granting licenses. This had something to do with the constraints that came with higher education institutions accepting State and Federal financial support, and apparently nothing to do with our negotiating skills, so the best that we could do was to obtain a standard Non-Exclusive Royalty-Free (so-called 'NERF') license to the IP.

However, I knew that the university IP portfolio was like Swiss cheese: full of holes. This was understandable and due to the cost of obtaining patents that the university preferred to avoid—which, when all was said and done, could run up to as much as an eye-watering $100,000. The university policy was to focus on discoveries that were either pure physics or were in some way demonstrably fundamental, and to leave the patents pertaining to application methods to commercial entities.

So Aram and I filed a couple of incremental claims and assigned them to Mak'Ur AI, Inc. These were based on the residual knowledge that we carried in our heads and that completed the technology that we had developed at the university—things like the design of an analog neural processor, or some of the 2.5D integration techniques. This was a bit like patenting the key to the door of a walled garden. Once we'd described it in those terms, even Stiglitz agreed to support the unplanned costs. Fortunately, those turned out to be quite modest—nowhere near $100K—because Aram and I had all the information at our fingertips, making the necessary background searches quite trivial.

We did have to be careful to stay away from anything that could be construed as derivative of the university's IP, so we engaged a specialist legal firm to help us focus on patenting the keys to a door rather than something to do with the walled garden itself, to extend the analogy. Even after dealing with all the details that were involved in preparing a patent claim, it took us only a couple of months. We filed our claims with USPO but decided to save some money and postponed filing with the EU or some of the Asian patent offices.

After that, Mak'Ur AI, Inc. had de-facto exclusive access to all of the university's AI intellectual property, which was a very good position, and definitely an edge versus the other AI startups. Or so we thought…

Once we consolidated our IP position, Aram thought that Mak'Ur should also push some of the industry standards. Standards enable interoperability between products from different vendors, and as such are absolutely essential for a class of technologies being adopted by the industry at large. Without standards, everyday products like PCs and phones would be impossible.

Anyway, this was something that Aram was dead set on. He insisted that a key part of the corporate strategy was to ensure that Mak'Ur technology became baked into the various AI standards that the industry was developing. He was quite adamant that even if we had to give away our IP, we should pursue this approach. He argued that AI technology would inevitably be commoditized, and that in a commodity market owning standard-essential IP was bound to give us an edge. And he was clearly hoping that the company would be able to charge some kind of license fees for access to industry standard IP—even if we had to share it with the university. He'd read a few books on the topic and kept bringing up the example of Qualcomm and its licensing fees in the mobile telephony market.

In the end we agreed that we should give it a go. It was a bit odd—a startup getting involved with standards—but Aram felt it was strategic. However, regardless how good the strategy sounded, its implementation was a lot harder. I dug into it and quickly found that the world of standards for Artificial Intelligence was a bit of Wild West in nature. There were all sorts of bodies—government institutions, ad hoc committees, trade groups, associations and professional societies—generating all kinds of standards for Artificial Intelligence, ranging from abstract to mundane. From top level standards focused on the general use of AI in society, and defining things like the ethical practices for use of AI in medicine, law enforcement, self-driving cars—somewhat reminiscent of Isaac Asimov's Three Laws of Robotics, down to nitpicky standards that defined how AI hardware and software were to be benchmarked and labeled, and everything else in between.

The standards that were of interest to us were those that dictated the format of the hardware and software interfaces to be used in AI systems, those that defined the protocols for system training, and those that defined the requirements for the various tiers of privacy and security levels. The type of standards that chips and the associated software for systems that learned on the fly and modified their behavior through field use would have to meet.

Such standards were normally managed by the IEEE and/ or JEDEC, and similar professional bodies. Joining these organizations was trivial—just a bit of money for an appropriate membership fee. And even that could often be deferred for a small company like Mak'Ur.

The hard part was the time and patience that the actual participation in the standard setting committees required. It was onerous work—slow, tedious and pedantic. Not to mention that it was boring, soul numbing and quite time consuming. And that it required listening to and even humoring the stupidest of ideas of some people on the committee. It took only a couple of meetings and reviews of the associated paperwork to convince me that there was no way that I could do it by myself. It was clear that if we were to integrate our IP into the industry AI standards, we had to hire a dedicated engineer or two, which explained why startups tended not to get involved with standardization early in the corporate development cycle.

This precipitated an internal mini war. Aram was supportive—even insistent—on hiring people to drive the standardization effort. But Stiglitz protested that this would be another unplanned expense and that we could not afford it. He said that he absorbed the cost of filing the patents, but that there was no way we could include extra headcount in our budget. Aram insisted that this was more important than the office space or some of our planned travel expenses, and that we should look for savings elsewhere.

"Not under current constraints. Out of the question!" Stiglitz responded. "It simply cannot be done now. We will have to postpone it until we have more funding, or until we have a revenue stream that could support such an expense."

He repeated this mantra every time the subject came up and explained that we were burning through cash faster than expected. Office costs, travel costs, market report costs, patents, our salaries... Aram and I tried to argue that this was because we were developing the company's position faster than expected, but Stiglitz insisted that there was no money for additional staff until at least the fourth quarter.

Inevitably, this came up as an issue during one of our face-to-face meetings with Tigran. We had those whenever he came to the States—maybe a couple of hours every quarter or so. Other than that, as far as I could tell Tigran channeled all of his interest in Mak'Ur through his avatar: Stiglitz. However, Tigran's reaction surprised me. I expected that he would side with Stiglitz, but instead he asked us to explain, and he listened carefully to make sure that he understood. Then he asked about the kind of engineers that would be required, the kind of work that needed to be done, and so forth. I mean, he really got down to the essential aspects. He then said that he would think about it, that he may have some ideas, and that he would discuss it with Stiglitz off-line.

A few days later Stiglitz announced that Tigran's other businesses were flourishing and that Tigran had agreed to accommodate our needs with some 'off the books' money. "But," he said, "the new hires will have to be in Yerevan. That is the only way that Tigran can make it work."

That floored me. What the hell was I going to do with an engineer in Yerevan?

And I was also confused about what 'off the books money' meant, and asked Stiglitz to explain it. But he just waved the question away and said something like, "actual cost will be carried by Tigran's local Armenian operations, but the reported cost will be a Mak'Ur AI expense item." He gave me a knowing look and a nudge, as if there was something that I should read between the lines. "It is blue money," he added, as if to clarify. All that meant nothing to me, so I let it go.

Making such an arrangement work, with an engineer in Yerevan, me in the US, and the standard body meetings taking place in various places around the globe was of far greater concern to me. It seemed to be a logistical and management nightmare. I was skeptical.

And I was also concerned about hiring the right engineer. It had to be someone not only conversant in, but also deeply familiar with AI technology and terminology. After all, as far as the standards community was concerned, he—or she—would be the face of the company. Our engineer would have to have sufficient experience and gravitas to interact intelligently with the rest of the people on the committees who were often heavyweights in their own right. In addition he would have to be willing to work on tedious things that engineers—especially the kind of engineers that I was hoping to hire—rarely found worthy of their time and talents.

I voiced my concerns. Aram was no help, and uncharacteristically remained quiet. Stiglitz, however, suggested that I write a specification for the position: required education, knowledge, experience, personality attributes, temperament, and so forth. He thought that if we could not find anyone suitable in Yerevan then perhaps Tigran would support hiring someone in the US.

Much to my surprise, within a couple of weeks I had phone interviews with six candidates who all seemed very qualified, top notch people—some with degrees from US universities and even with years of experience with US companies. After a few rounds of two, three and even four-way conversations, and a quick on-site visit, we settled on Alex Alexanian. He had an excellent knowledge of English, was quite articulate and familiar with AI principles, and even experienced in working with standards bodies. He was perfect for the position. Mak'Ur Employee number one.

At the time it did not occur to me to question how Tigran had found such attractive candidates, and how he had managed to convince such competent professionals to work for an unheard-of startup like Mak'Ur.

And a couple of months later we hired Sedrak Sargisian—also based in Yerevan. Alex convinced us that if we were to be successful, then there was too much to do; and that if we were to do standards right and actively participate in that many committees, he would need help. As it turned out, he happened to know just a right candidate, the proverbial: "I have a cousin who..."Yet, Sedrak was a superb fit.

Surprisingly, Stiglitz and Tigran did not seem to have a problem with it. And I certainly was not going to argue against hiring people. So we did! Employee number two!

Mak'Ur AI, Inc. already had a satellite office in Yerevan with two employees.

OBJECTIVE 2:
MARKET ANALYSES

It did not take us long—maybe a few months to find our feet, so to speak—until we had to embrace the 'joys' of travel. Of course we tried to do as much of the work as possible by phone and e-mail, but the kind of conversations that we wanted to have required face-to-face contact.

An essential part of our strategy was to get a feel for the market before we dove into product development. We had the technology down and knew exactly what we needed to do and how to do it. That was not the problem for us. We had all kinds of market trend reports and projections that Stiglitz obtained from various industry analysts and consultants for as much as $10K a pop, and so we understood the global landscape. That was not the problem either. The problem for us was that we were facing a blank slate when it came to positioning our technology within the market. We had the 'how' but not the 'what.' We needed a killer product, and to get that we obviously had to do our market research. And for that we had to meet and talk with all sorts of people: analysts and industry gurus; hands-on practitioners, as well as potential users; maverick pioneers, technologists and skeptics; hardware and software suppliers; business managers; supply chain managers; sales and marketing people. All sorts...

Fortunately, my name, stature, and connections still meant enough to open many doors. Between my ex-students and the network of people I met on the conference circuit, I found that with a few phone calls I could get an invitation to almost anywhere. Unfortunately, most of those 'doors' were on the West Coast—some in Texas, some in New England, but mostly on the West Coast. I traveled abroad, too—China, Japan, Korea, and Europe.

We had our work cut out for us and in those days I pretty much lived on airplanes. To manage costs it was mostly me who did the travelling, mostly alone. On occasion Aram, or even Aram plus Stiglitz, came along depending on the nature of a meeting, but I did most of the actual interfacing.

We quickly realized that managing meeting schedules was a logistical nightmare. People we wanted to talk with were busy, and finding an open slot on their calendar was hard enough even without trying to align the openings on the calendars of multiple people. So, being the engineers that we were, we developed a systematic approach: instead of trying to fit our travel around the calendars of the busy people we wanted to meet, we turned the problem upside down and first scheduled regular trips then worked the meetings into one of the time slots when we were in a given area, much like the classic travelling salesman problem. We tried to synch up our travel with the various industry conferences and expos, which were also convenient venues for meeting people. To manage our priorities and conflicts we even developed a weighted rating system based on the given individual's affiliation and rank in an organization. Altogether we had a complex mechanism for managing our schedules.

On the positive side, this approach made Stiglitz happy, since we could book our travel well ahead of time rather than traveling ad-hoc—which saved a considerable amount on airfares. On the negative side, it meant that I had to be on the road every other week. I was surprised that it added up to half-time, but given the number of people we had to meet, and the time that we had to do it in, that was how it worked out

Bev was certainly not happy with me being gone half the time, and I could not blame her, because I was not happy with being gone half the time either. Alone in our house, and with Lara gone away to college and me on the road, rendered a double empty-nest syndrome. Having the house to herself every now and then may have been fun—I know that I enjoyed it in the past when she and Lara went somewhere for a weekend, but half of the time alone in an empty house? She put up a brave face and said something about it being nice that the house would be clean for a change, but her eyes told a different story. I told her that it had to be so—at least for three to six months—and, bless her supportive heart, she understood and accepted it.

Besides, we tried to compensate for my absences. When I was at home we shared coffee time in bed, or a nice big breakfast together, or occasionally a morning walk in the neighborhood. In addition, we took frequent weekend trips. Altogether, I felt that our relationship was adjusting nicely to my new and hopefully temporary reality.

Still, all that business travel was a pain in the ass. I'd envisioned myself as something of a road warrior when I was a professor looking for donors, but as it turned out, that was nothing. Spending half my time on the road meant waking up alone in a strange bed as often as next to Bev in my own bed. It meant hotel bathrooms of dubious cleanliness, greasy breakfasts in local diners, hours in airports and more hours on airplanes. And the persistent lack of movement: sitting in various meetings, sitting in cars, sitting in waiting lounges, sitting... At times it was so bad that I really regretted my decision to leave the comfortable cocoon of the university. "Idiot!" I berated myself, especially when things did not go to plan, as inevitably they often didn't. Delayed flights, last minute meeting cancellations, traffic jams...

At a particularly low point, one long, wet and depressing night in a hotel somewhere in the Bay Area sometime in March or April—the kind of night when no amount of heat could drive out the dampness from my bones—I did come very close to quitting. I felt like I just could not take another day of that lifestyle. I even wrote a letter of resignation, but I could not—and did not—quit. Partially because my pride would not allow me to admit that I'd made a mistake—especially not only a few months into this misadventure—and, I admit, partially due to concern over Tigran's reaction to my breaking of the commitment that he'd made us swear to. It was not that I was afraid for my life and limb—not back then. Back then I was more concerned about losing face and admitting defeat, disappointing Aram, and maybe earning an enemy in Tigran...

But, over time things got better. Stiglitz found a furnished apartment in the Bay Area—I think it was some deal he worked out through Air BnB. This was not only nicer than staying in hotels, but also worked out to be cheaper given the amount of time we were spending there. And seeing that the cost of a stay was fixed and constant, we were not under pressure to squeeze all the meetings into the minimum time possible just to save a few hundred bucks on hotel costs. So we could organize more humane schedules that even allowed time for exercise, for some R and R, for home cooked meals... Altogether everything seemed better.

The overseas trips were a grueling tradeoff too. We felt that with a globalized market we would be getting an incomplete picture if we did not reach out to suitable people and entities abroad. So we had to organize multiple trips to Asia; to Japan and China, and to Taiwan and Korea. And we did a separate trip to England and Germany. These trips were a lot of work to set up and absolutely exhausting to live through. Hours on transoceanic flights squeezed into tiny economy-class seats that barely allowed you to shift your weight; trying to put together last-minute fixes to our presentation, with the laptop flat on the belly, because the passenger in front had lowered his seat all the way back; coping with a cabin that was sometimes freezing cold and sometimes stuffy hot; balancing a drink or a meal on those tiny trays when some idiot in your row decided to go to the restroom during mealtime; and of course, trying to survive on the so-called airplane food—altogether quite horrible!

Often, after all those hours spent on the planes, I would not see much more than the insides of meeting rooms. The way schedules were arranged, I would usually have to turn around and fly right back without ever adjusting to the new time zone. Such a waste, it seemed, after travelling halfway around the globe.

We used the meetings to probe people on their thoughts and suggestions and comments and... Interaction with the real professionals in the industry were not at all like the lectures and conferences that had dominated my past life, or like reading academic papers or gathering data in the lab. This felt more like drinking from a fire hose.

The whirlwind of meetings with various people produced a veritable kaleidoscope of impressions. In order to precipitate actionable lessons, we found that we had to sift through all the data, observations and comments immediately after the meetings—before the learning dissipated into vague memories. Aram insisted that we hold post meeting reviews, which helped. We met religiously by phone after every meeting, and in person after every trip. Aram also demanded that we conduct those reviews in a disciplined and structured way. He made us write everything down. He read several books on sales and even made up a cheat-sheet that he wanted us to fill out after every meeting—org chart, economic buyer, technical buyer, coach, champion, anxiety point, key value proposition—to be presented and discussed in our reviews. He mumbled things about needing a record that could be revisited at some future date when our memories may not be quite as clear, and he even toyed around with putting it all in some kind of an interactive computer database, and spent considerable effort trying to implement something of the kind. I felt that a lot of his rigor was a bit too bureaucratic, but I humored him. After all, he was the boss, and demanding this structure was within his rights whether I agreed or disagreed. However it was all digested, the learning opened entirely new horizons for me.

Sometimes these meetings would even generate an emotional high—almost like being drunk or on drugs. When I realized that I'd managed to convert a skeptical audience into a group of supporters and even believers, it was quite an ego trip. And when I'd digested the feedback from some industry luminary and realized that he or she agreed with me, these were not only assurances that we were on the right path but also emotional highs, and it became quite addictive.

And I admit that I also enjoyed the wining and dining part. Taking, or extending, some of our meetings in local fine dining restaurants was the norm—especially in Asia. For a good reason. Often it was the only way we could get to meet some people. And often, we learned more in those settings than in a formal meeting in some conference room. Maybe it was the general sense of wellbeing precipitated by a gourmet meal, and ample servings of the finest wines. Or maybe it was just the old *in vino veritas*. On occasions like that people's guard was down and they often said more than they probably intended to say. Or maybe it was that those meetings tended to leave a stronger impression on me. Whatever it was, I thrived in that environment.

Of course, Stiglitz was not happy with the bills—often more than a thousand dollars for a single dinner event. Sometimes much more. But it was the way of the world... And I noticed that he complained less on those occasions when he joined us.

On the whole—and certainly so looking at it in the rear-view mirror—the agony and the ecstasy of travel, and all that went with it, was well worth it. We met with just about everybody who was anybody in the business—both in the US and abroad—and picked up all kinds of perspectives. We definitely learned a lot, and a clear picture of market realities began to emerge in our minds.

AN OFFER WE
COULD REFUSE

An unexpected consequence of all those meetings was that Mak'Ur was actually beginning to be noticed. I guess in a provincial industry like ours, driven by a highly interconnected workforce who seemed to enjoy gossiping, it should not have been such a surprise. In fact, I routinely received calls from various people—mostly ex-students and colleagues—who seemed to have heard about Mak'Ur through the rumor mill, and who seemed to just want to cheer us on. And, I suspect, to be noticed— presumably in case we were successful and they needed a job or an 'in' of some kind. Simple networking; but these were from people I knew.

It was not that we got a mention in the industry press, or even received random inquiries to our central number, or hits to our web page. Those would have been nice but hard to do back then since we were still more or less in stealth mode, and most of our internet site consisted of blank pages that simply stated: 'under construction.' We did invest in developing a corporate web site, but mostly to reserve the appropriate names and URL addresses—something that Stiglitz took care of through a contract with an Armenian software outfit for a paltry $1,000. But other than the bios and contact information for the three founders the site remained blank. Even the 'about' page was on hold for a precise vision.

No, the notice that surprised me was a cold call from a company I'd never heard of—an outfit called Nager AI, Ltd. based in Dublin, Ireland. Their founder and CEO, Atul Sharan, called to say that he had heard about Mak'Ur through the industry grapevine and suggested that perhaps we should meet to discuss opportunities to collaborate. I, of course, readily accepted. Not just as a professional courtesy, but also because I found the call surprising and somewhat flattering. We zeroed in on a date.

I looked them up right after we hung up and learned that they were also focused on Artificial Intelligence and Machine Learning with emphases on Edge based computing. From what I could gather, they were also a startup, but a few years ahead of us in the development cycle—apparently founded in 2015, and Round-A funded in 2016 for an undisclosed amount. However, beyond the baseline fact that both entities seemed to be targeting Edge based AI, I did not see much overlap. They seemed to be focused more on the software side of things, and our tendency was to lean toward the hardware side. Still, it was early days, and I thought that it was possible that some opportunity might arise. Besides, it was just dinner.

We met a couple of weeks later and shared a leisurely talk about our respective businesses, strategies, and products. I liked Atul. He was one of those bi-continental people, with offices— and homes—in Dublin, Ireland, and Palo Alto, California. He seemed to spend equal amounts of time in each, so a stopover on the US East Coast was more or less on the way for him. His company—Nager Ltd.—was based in the Bay Area, as most of his operations and staff were there, except for the headquarters and the business office. These were in Ireland due to favorable tax laws, and also because his investors, and some of his major clients, were European and Middle Eastern.

We met a few more times and it became clear that what had attracted his attention were our patents and proposed standards. Atul eventually revealed that whereas their product was a software system for edge computing, their primary backer was in fact interested in building a patent portfolio in AI domain, which led me to eventually realize that they were basically a troll company. The software business was just a front, or a sideline. That obviously turned me off, but Atul was persistent and in the end floated an offer to acquire Mak'Ur for a couple of million dollars.

This was of course a tentative offer pending all sorts of due diligence, but it was all there in black and white in a formal Letter of Intent that he presented to me. This was a bit presumptuous, I thought. Like most engineers I despised trolls and thought that the disparaging tag that the industry gave them described them very well. Atul did not seem to notice anything and just kept on talking about the pot of money that his investors had put at his disposal and the returns that he expected to reap once the industry settled down and standard practices and lead players emerged. I presumed that those would be his targets, and in hindsight, it was clearly our early investment in developing AI industry standards that had brought us to his attention.

To put it mildly, I was flabbergasted. But selling out at this stage was not on my horizon. Not for any amount of money.

Nevertheless, I called a partners' meeting to formally describe the offer. It seemed like the right thing to do no matter how I personally felt about it.

We met in our conference room—with Tigran participating on the phone. It was late—maybe around 11:00 at night—corresponding to 8:00 am Paris time, since Tigran was in France at the time. I described the offer in as unbiased and objective terms as I could, while reserving my personal views for the actual discussion.

Stiglitz was impressed that our investment in Mak'Ur patents seemed to be producing a return of about 100x. I thought that this missed the point and that he was looking at it in narrow, short term financial terms only. I explained that by definition the value of Intellectual Property—the right kind of intellectual property—should of course always total much more than the cost of filing the patents. I might have been a bit too harsh on him, because he just shrugged and clammed up after that.

Aram was surprised—just as I was. After spluttering for a while, mostly expressing his incredulity at the offer, he ended up protesting that the offer was nowhere near the potential value of the company, and that we should of course ignore it. "Give us a year or two, and we should be able to beat that offer by another hundred times!" he stated confidently.

I suspect that at least a part of Aram's internal reasoning was also that he had no alternatives in his life. That even if he was a millionaire, once we sold Mak'Ur he would basically have no other options than to start up another company that looked, smelled and sounded just like Mak'Ur AI, Inc. From his perspective, selling out would in fact be a step backwards, and there was no point in doing so regardless of the gains realized in such a short time.

I thought—and said—that whereas the few hundred thousand that each of us would make by selling the company at this early stage would be gratifying, selling to a troll was like selling to a devil. That it would be a wrong—if not immoral—thing to do. Frankly, I was with Aram, and did not like the idea of going back to academia even if I was a few hundred thousand dollars richer.

Ultimately, we all knew that it was really up to Tigran. I could see how an investor—perhaps a more usual investor than Tigran—might have liked the idea of realizing a healthy gain after only a few months, cashing out, and moving on to the next thing. When all was said and done, he would have made somewhere between five to ten times his original investment.

Tigran listened to our arguments and perspectives and said nothing. When we'd each spent our bullets, so to speak, and fell silent, he cleared his throat and delivered his judgment.

"You know," he said in his typical slow cadence, "in my part of the world an offer like this would be seen as an insult. It would be interpreted like someone saying that they thought that they were smarter than you, and that they could make more money out of *your* business than you could. A challenge to your abilities, and to your manhood... So, not so many years ago, in my part of the world, the response to an offer like this would have to be quite forceful. Maybe bombing his offices or eliminating some of his known minions, or something equally convincing... To send a message that you had the balls to protect your business, to stand your ground. Unless, of course, the offer came from someone so obviously more powerful than you, that accepting it would be the only graceful response. The unstated alternative clearly would have been that it would be *your* home that would be bombed..." He trailed off.

What? I was flabbergasted. What was he talking about?

Bombing? Eliminating minions? Which century was he living in?

But instead of expressing my amazement, I assured him that none of that would be necessary and that we could simply say 'no thank you' and move on.

Tigran burst into an uproarious laugh, and between all the uncontrolled sporadic chuckles said something about it just being a joke. "You Americans should not take things so literally," he added, obviously trying hard to regain his composure.

Eventually he calmed down and concluded in a very matter-of-fact way: "I did not get involved with this technology business to make a million or two. No! I do not care who we sell out to but I am in this to make a *billion* dollars. So, no, I am not for selling out. Not to this Nager AI, or to anyone, for only a couple of million."

And that was that.

Tigran was clearly willing to keep funding us, so we—I might add, happily and quite relieved —unanimously agreed to turn down the unexpected offer and to carry on.

THE BUSINESS STRATEGY

The world of AI was huge, and a part of our challenge was to tie our technology to a specific product. We had an answer that was looking for a problem. The fact that our technology was flexible and was therefore applicable to many product ideas did not help. We needed to pick a single one and make that work. Through many meetings and market studies we precipitated some key conclusions.

First, we felt that we had acquired the clarity needed to select our target market—the so-called smart-home segment as opposed to industrial applications, office space, data analytics in the cloud, smart-car, gaming, finances and banking, law enforcement, or any of the myriad of other AI application spaces that people in the industry were talking about. The smart-home space was compatible with our core value propositions: relatively low-cost solution with scalable Lego-block hardware focused on edge-processing. Furthermore, it became clear that the smart-home market was not yet quite ready for the kind of a product that we had in mind. That was good for us because we were still a few years away from realizing it. And, according to all the studies and reports that Stiglitz procured, it was a market segment that was expected to experience very rapid growth over the next decade or so, potentially reaching huge volumes. And volume was the other side of the low-cost coin which we would need to fuel the growth of Mak'Ur.

We also decided to pursue the B2B business mode. We would not try to compete directly in the consumer market to reach end customers for smart-home appliances and associated gizmos; we would instead be a business-to-business AI supplier to existing appliance makers, home system integrators, and other entities that already had a suitable distribution network in the consumer market. In that way we would avoid the overhead required to compete on Main Street and still reach the end users.

Last but not least, we converged on a target concept product based on what we thought would be the most attractive packaging of our core technology. We felt that the players in this segment would be most open to a stand-alone box that would enable all the AI-specialized capabilities—such as the pre-training and the on-the-fly-learning—and that would integrate their appliances to a phone or a PC through a given user interface, leveraging the usual WiFi, or mobile network or wired connections. Sort of like the set-top box used to connect the TV to the internet, but specialized for running AI applications, and configurable for a given set of smart-home subsystems. In our case it would consist mostly of our multi-chip module and a set of input and output ports. We could almost fit it on a USB stick format, and we thought that this kind of a product would be efficient and cost effective since it would leverage everything that was already out there and reproduce nothing that our clients were building.

However, on the downside we learned that all AI opportunities, including the smart-home market, were not just about hardware—not just about building a better mouse trap. It was more about integration and user friendliness and the ease of a one-box, plug-and-play solution—AI Hardware plus AI software plus downloadable apps plus user friendly GUI, plus on the fly remote learning—all on top of that better mouse trap.

An example that stuck in my mind came from a manufacturer of home security systems. This company and their requirements somehow served as an anchor point that tethered the undefined big AI opportunity to something that was specific and concrete. The fact that the CEO of that company was a very attractive lady, in a dominatrix power-frau kind of a way, may have had something to do with it. In some down moment I visualized her in an Elvira type of a revealing outfit, smoking one of those slim cigars and sounding like Lauren Bacall. I shared the thought with Stiglitz and Aram, who looked her up on the web and started joking about photo-shopping her face onto an Elvira pin-up poster that we could then use as a picture of our company's best clients to be posted in the corporate reception area. All joking aside, the name stuck (far more appealing than her real Dr. Barbara Vasquez) and we invariably referred to her as Elvira, and of course her company became Elvira, Inc. in all our notes, records and conversations. Her looks notwithstanding, she was quite sharp, articulate, and remarkably clear and crisp about where she wanted to take her business.

Anyway, her company had already established a position in the home security market. They had a complete system that included cameras, motion and audio sensors, a wireless link to a computer, and software that managed the system and the associated records. She wanted to upgrade their system with AI capabilities without having to hire engineers to re-invent the wheel, and therefore wanted to partner with an AI specialist to complement their capabilities and produce a turn-key solution.

And she had a wish list. The system had to be pre-trained with capabilities to differentiate between common false threats versus real threats: not only a cat versus a person, but an old harmless lady versus a toothless meth addict. And she wanted the system to be capable of learning on the fly, so it could distinguish between regular visitors—a mailman, or nosy neighbor, versus someone unknown. Further, she wanted to be able to interface the system to a database in the cloud, from which she could download known threats such as the latest alerts from the police or a local neighborhood network, or known safe identities such as Amazon and UPS drivers working in the area. She also wanted the system to have full speech recognition, learn language patterns and accents, and differentiate between the voice commands from known sources as opposed to those of strangers, and to respond appropriately and accordingly. She felt that some level of personalization and a 'cutesy factor' would be required to make it sell—like the ability to give the system a name and some form of a personality.

The entire system had to interface to a phone and/or a laptop through a handy app, and it had to be simple to operate and intuitive enough so that even a housewife in Podunk, Indiana, would not be intimidated by it. It had to be smart enough to guide the user through all the programming steps and to be able to interface purely through two-way speech communication. The system she wanted would be completely voice command driven offering superior security to PIN codes.

Similarly, on the reaction side, she wanted the system to intelligently classify the nature of an intrusion and to decide whether to unlock the doors and turn on the welcoming lights, or to send an alert to an owner's phone, raise an alarm, call the police, ambulance, or whatever might be appropriate.

She also anticipated features such as 'smart delivery,' where the system was capable of being aware of the contents of a given order and would recognize trusted delivery such as a known Doordash driver, unlock the door and ask him or her to drop off the package in a fridge or the oven. Or have a pre-defined 'safe word,' which a known user could mutter to raise the alarm and call 911 in case of an armed intrusion or an accident. Brave new world. A home truly smart enough to be more like a partner. She also thought that the only way something like that could be competitive was nothing short of the economies of scale derived from competing on a global market.

Her wish list seemed straight forward, but even a superficial assessment quickly indicated that such a system would have to be armed with some impressive AI capabilities and include state of the art image processing for facial recognition, along with audio analytics for speech recognition capabilities. The technology appeared simple enough, but for that application it could pose some serious pre-training challenges. And the system would have to be sensitive to local variations—for example, different for the Asian market as opposed to the US market; or even a rural versus an urban setting. It would need to process different languages, accents, idioms and so forth, and the system would have to have sufficient local processing power to enable all the subsequent in-use learning, and to make sure its operation was seamless and secure. Plus, it would have to have the ability to make the necessary response decisions on the spot without the latency and security issues associated with relying on the cloud. But an interface to a cloud was required, not only for all the pre-training, but also for downloading the current threat information without compromising privacy and security. All in a single package that would have to be easy to train and use and update. And at a relatively low cost. Easily definable, but in fact quite a tall order.

Of course, we were sure that our scalable hardware technology with multi-chip modules that could be cheaply configured to match a given set of requirements was ideally suited to this kind of application. It could be easily customized for, say, a single-family residence or a multi-family establishment, number and types of sensors in the security system, type of neighborhood, and so on...

On the negative side, we realized that we did not have a solution for the software. We knew that there were existing algorithms out there for things like face and voice recognition. Alexa and DeepFace and Siri were obvious examples. Many were available in smartphones or as a downloadable app. We planned to fully leverage all those, rather than writing our own. But to do that we needed an integrated software platform that seamlessly included the best of everything, while ensuring complete privacy and security. That was not so easy.

It was clear that without a solution for this gap we did not have a viable business. We were technology people—maybe architecture people—but not software geeks. Yet the market feedback was clear. There was no point having an elegant modular hardware solution without having an equally elegant and modular software solution. The market wisdom suggested that it was the software that won a customer's attention, so that must come first; and it was the hardware that won their wallets, so that came second. This obviously posed a big problem for us.

We spent a lot of BTU's wrestling with it. It came to a head during one of our many meetings. It was sometime in mid-summer and it was late—maybe 10:00 o'clock at night. A deserted parking lot and distant city lights shimmered in the window of our conference room. An empty pizza box lay on the table.

With the smell of pepperoni still lingering in the air, we reached an impasse.

Nobody wanted to say it aloud, but I was sure that it was on all of our minds. "Maybe there is no business opportunity for hardware people like us," I suggested. "Maybe we were wrong from the start, and in the absence of some slick software, we should fold and stop throwing good money—and time—after bad."

Of course, this went over like a lead balloon. Both Aram and Stiglitz stared coldly at me. Aram's look was bordering on hostility—maybe even hate.

"No way!" he responded, slapping the table and almost shouting. "I am not giving up now. I believe that now that we have learned what we have learned, we have that much more knowledge than before. Which means that we are that much better positioned to make Mak'Ur fly!"

"That may be so in principle," I responded, "but in reality it is clear to me that we need software. And what do we know about software? Nothing! It is a must have to be competitive. These are the inescapable facts, not a rose-colored analysis based on wishful thinking."

Aram and I stared at each other like two roosters ready to fight. We often had lively debates where one of us would champion the opposite side of whatever the other was proposing, and we were about to get into it. But then Stiglitz spoke up.

"Why don't we just go out and get the software?"

Aram and I turned to face him, and before we managed to blow him off with our usual comments about him not understanding the technology, he continued, "Think about it. We need some knowledge that we do not have. So what? Let's go out and get it. You two are so used to being the smartest people in the room that you're stumped when you aren't. The rest of us are used to that kind of a situation. So listen to me..."

Such an outburst was quite unusual for Stiglitz.

"There are thousands of software shops out there," he carried on. "Like the outfit that built our web site. There is no end to lone coders and mom and pop kind of shops. There are many ten to twenty-man software service companies, and there are giant corporations who take contracts. Any of them can write apps and custom software, and most are available for hire. They can provide services on an hourly basis, or they can be engaged on contract. Or, for that matter, they can be bought out entirely. Why don't we simply use one of those?"

Both Aram and I were speechless. This was not something that had occurred to either of us.

"In fact," Stiglitz hurried before we shut him down, "Yerevan is full of shops like that. Altogether, Eastern Europe—from Serbia to Armenia and everything in between has numerous software teams for hire. Ukraine, Poland, Romania... I read about them in those market analysis reports that we bought. They are apparently high quality and fueled by many excellent universities which are churning out new coders by the thousands. Even big companies like Google and Microsoft use them. To boot, the cost of these Eastern European software teams is five to ten times lower than in the EU or here. So, why don't we just sub-contract the software?"

Stiglitz pressed his point: "All they need is a project. Point them in the right direction and they will work with you to define a spec, and then to fully implement it in whatever language, format or application framework that you require. Quite simply, they are guns for hire. Pay them properly and presto! You get whatever you want." Stiglitz closed triumphantly.

"But what about the money?" I challenged, feeling the need to extend our adversarial advocate practice to Stiglitz too. "You gave us grief about hiring Alex and Sedrak. Contracting a software company—even somewhere in Eastern Europe—for a project like this is bound to cost plenty."

"True," Stiglitz allowed. "It certainly cannot be done within our existing budget. But if we can tie this new expenditure to some incremental revenue with a shorter fuse, then maybe..."

"What 'shorter fuse?'" I asked, genuinely interested.

"Well, if I understand you techies correctly, time to money for a hardware product is of the order of two to three years from the starting point. Right? Tigran's current funding plan is based on that assumption. But with software, maybe time to money could be shorter. Say a year, or even less...

"If so, then maybe Tigran would be willing to invest more

money faster. Shorter time to money means lower risk."

We both stared at Stiglitz with newly found respect. Certainly, he had grown in stature in my eyes. I loved the way he thought. So different than Aram or me. And so very useful at that moment...

OBJECTIVE 3:
THE BUSINESS PLAN

A few weeks later, out of the blue, Aram set up a formal 'partners' meeting' (his choice of words); a working dinner set for the Friday before Labor Day at the Mak'Ur offices. The meeting was scheduled to coincide with Tigran's visit to the States. He said he wanted to share something with all of us and was ordering food from the Armenian Nights restaurant and bragged about bringing some fancy Armenian wine and Dvin brandy.

On one hand, this was certainly odd—and hence interesting and special. Normally, when we worked late and got hungry we just ordered pizza, or maybe burgers, but never a full meal, and especially not from a fancy place like Armenian Nights, accompanied by good wines and brandy. And we never ordered ahead of time. Then again, Tigran did not usually join our sessions.

It was a bit awkward, a late meeting on a Friday evening before a long weekend, as I had plans for a weekend outing with Bev. I asked what it was about, but Aram just grinned and said that we would have to wait to find out.

So on that Friday, the three partners plus Stiglitz gathered in our conference room. Aram was positively beaming with an ear to ear grin. His black eyes shone with excitement. Clearly keyed up he fidgeted even more than usual. But he insisted on having our dinners first, poured the wine, and chatted amiably, as if we were four buddies out for a meal. Stiglitz and I were happy to play along as we enjoyed the food and wine. Tigran was atypically silent, obviously waiting to hear what Aram had to say.

When the dinner was done, and we cleared away all the debris, Aram brought out the Armenian brandy. Then, finally, he dimmed the lights and started his presentation. The first slide said in big bold letters:

Mak'Ur AI = Make *Your* AI

Seeing our blank stares he elaborated, "That is to be our tag line. How do you gentlemen like it? Pure luck that it matches so well with our name... Get it? Mak'Ur is a contracted version of *Make-Your*. We can probably work it into our logo and collateral material. Pretty cool, hey?"

I was underwhelmed. It was cute, but so what? It was certainly not worth all the pomp and anticipation.

Aram continued, undaunted: "A tagline is just the tip of the marketing iceberg. But I believe that this one captures the spirit of what I want to communicate—that we are a holistic, one-stop-shop for *customizable* AI solutions!"

Tigran, Stiglitz and I remained silent as he spoke.

"For the first time since we started," Aram explained, "I have a complete and clear vision for our company. I think I am ready for a pitch for our Series-A investment round. Hear me out.

"One," he flashed up another slide and continued, "Mak Ur AI shall enter the market as a software provider. We shall develop software for home appliance vendors—software that will be the backbone for a future smart-home, and that can connect any and every given smart-appliance into an AI-enabled smart-home *system*..."

"Ok-a-a-a-y," I hesitated, not so excited about us being a software company.

"We will *Make Your AI Infrastructure*," he inserted, stressing the tagline, before I could elaborate on my reluctance. "We will offer a backbone software package that can be customized for every aspect of a future smart-home. Security system, or lighting control, or climate control, or even management of individual appliances like vacuum cleaners and mowers, kitchen and laundry appliances... With a unified architecture, a shared software wrapper, GUI interface, and the like, to be run on any standard home PC."

"How?" I challenged.

"We shall do it by licensing existing best-in-class software packages and integrating them into a solution specialized for smart-home applications, probably by contracting, partnering and/or acquiring a software capability. Or maybe using a blend of one of Stiglitz's Eastern European shops and some local hires."

"Ok-a-a-a-y," I hesitated again, and wondered inwardly if this was another instance of Aram buying into his own wishful thinking. I, too, had spent time checking out the web sites of those software service companies in Eastern Europe, but certainly was not ready to bet the business on our ability to find a good ready-made team that could execute to the vision that he was outlining.

"Two," he moved on to next slide, ignoring my doubts, "we shall then execute a pivot and become what we are at our core—a hardware company. We have a proprietary integration technology that is ideally suited to implement a specific AI solution for the smart-home market. And we can 'Make Your AI' chip." He stressed the tagline again, and emphasized, "Uniquely, we can make a custom multi-chip module and put it in a box that would turn your tired old home PC, or phone, into a smart-home hub that uses AI technology and methodology to intelligently manage any mix of appliances and home systems. It will be a customized and optimized smart-home solution at the price of a commodity product."

I liked this better but was still somewhat underwhelmed. "That is what we have been saying from the beginning..."

"True. I am just restating it," he agreed. "Making it fit into a holistic pitch. Bear with me..."

He moved on to the next slide and continued, "We will not make a profit on the base-line software. We will provide the software package to our clients as a loss-leader. It will be an offer that they cannot refuse—software at cost, or, for selected customers, even below cost. For any smart appliance and/or home-system manufacturer..."

"So how are we going to make money then?" Stiglitz spoke up, tentatively looking at Tigran.

Tigran, on the other hand, just listened and gestured for Stiglitz to wait.

"Well," Aram responded, seemingly ready for the question,

"we will use the software to break into the market and to position our company. It is sort of a pre-emptive pivot. If properly
architected, the *incremental* cost of a copy of a software package
is next to nothing. Especially if it is written leveraging an Eastern European cost structure. It will be a lot cheaper to give
away copies of software than to subsidize the hardware, or to
use any other cost-driven stratagem to break into a new market.
So, if we have to pay to enter the market, the cheapest way to
do that is through software. That is why we start there. We must
make it sufficiently attractive to all the appliance manufacturers
in order to end up becoming the default entity that defines the
AI backbone for our market. That is the key!"

Another slide and Aram carried on, "Strategically, it is critical
that our software becomes a dominant solution in the smart-
home market. For two reasons: first, it would give us access to
end user data that will enable us to make and/or train the best
AI software. Data is what makes AI work, so this access will
enable us to make the best solution. This is a virtuous cycle: the
more data we have, the better our solution, leading to a larger
market and to more data, and so on. It is the best way to domi-
nate the market and lock out the competition." He paused there
for effect, looking at each of us as if inviting (or daring) us to
question his analysis.

"Secondly," he continued, "the plan is to up-sell our hardware solution. Let's call it the 'AI Box,'" he made air quotes
for emphases, "to all our software users, so whoever installed
our software will be a natural customer for our hardware. In a
way, a very easy sell, since our AI Box will, by definition, be a
plug-and-play solution that can integrate all the appliances into
a true AI smart-home, at a lower cost than any alternative. Not
to mention that it will be better. The more software we install,
the larger the market for our hardware. We will have a leg up
and a ready-made market for the hardware just waiting for us
for when we are ready."

No one at the table spoke.

In reaction to our skeptical stares, he said, "Don't look at
me like I am saying something crazy. The idea of entering the
market at the low end, and using that to pave the way for more

expensive products has been practiced for years. Honda started by selling lawn mowers and worked their way into high end cars and now owns a larger percentage of the luxury car market than Cadillac. Ralph Lauren started by selling ties before getting into complete lines of clothing. It has all been done before.

"In fact," he continued to press his point, "a move from software to hardware is not so strange. Look at Google with its Chromebook Laptop and Pixel phones launched to monetize Chrome OS and Android. Or look at Microsoft with its X-Box. Or Amazon with Kindle e-reader... Been done before. The only difference would be that we are planning for this pivot ahead of time, as opposed to doing it in a response to the market conditions."

That made sense to me.

"So, after the pivot," he continued, "our revenue will be derived mostly from hardware sales—conventional dollars-per-AI Box model. It would take us two—maybe three—years from funding to tap into this revenue stream."

That part fit our preconceived ideas. Stiglitz and I looked at each other and nodded approvingly. Making money off the hardware was what our endeavor was supposed to be about.

"But," Aram continued, "we can also have multiple ways of augmenting this major revenue stream with earnings which can come online sooner.

"A: for a small incremental fee we can sell an app to end users—not to the appliance makers, but to *their* customers. Reaching out to customers' customers with a downloadable app has got to be a good strategic move for the company and its brand value. A slick app that includes all sorts of bells and whistles, so that they can play with their smart-appliances and all the data that this will generate. Something that they can show off to their neighbors. That has got to be the best way to turbo charge the entire smart-home market. The price would be low—say $9.99. Negligible when you are buying a $2,000 fridge, or whatever... It would put our brand on everybody's phone screen and the revenue would have scale, would be high margin, and could be ramped up the day that we enter the market. We will *Make Your AI App...*"

This idea was new, something we had never talked about, even though it committed us further into the software world.

"B," Aram carried on, "we can license access to our IP which, if we are successful at capturing the market, will define the standards required to integrate individual appliances into a true AI smart-home. A revenue stream that would also be very high margin and could be tapped into before our hardware comes online. We will *Make Your AI Interfaces...*"

Which prompted another slide...

"And, C," he finished, "we can also derive revenue by selling something like market consulting services. After all, if we execute well, we will be sitting on an extremely valuable data base. We would know pretty much everything there is to know about the homes and lives of our end users. Your fridge knows more about you than you realize. We will *Make Your AI Intros...*"

On the surface it seemed to me like the various bits of his go-to-market strategy fit well together, but...

"There", he turned off the projector, "we make *your* home smart. Software and Hardware. Infrastructure and Apps and Standards. Together or separate. Customized to *your* needs..."

He turned on the room lights and asked Stiglitz, "Can you make a version of your P&L projection spreadsheets to include all these revenue streams. Let's talk about the specific numbers when you have the basic structure."

Stiglitz nodded.

"And professor, could you work up architecture for an AI enabled security system, and then reach out to your Elvira lady friend to see if she would be interested in collaborating with us?"

I nodded assent too. Actually, I would just need to polish some of the ideas that we'd brainstormed—back of the envelope kind of stuff—only a few weeks before when we were digesting Elvira's inputs.

Then he topped up our brandy glasses, and with an expectant grin on his face asked, "So, what do you gentlemen think?"

I was busy trying to digest everything he'd said and to come up with reasons why his vision wouldn't work—just to accommodate the contrary way in which my mind operated and to fit the adversarial advocate pattern that Aram and I had established.

Tigran, on the other hand, nodded slowly, cleared his throat, and delivered his judgment.

"I like the multiple revenue streams," he evaluated in an even tone. "That is built-in business resilience. I like the marketing strategy, with relatively low-cost software paving the way for the high-margin hardware. That is clever. I like reaching out to customers' customers to build brand value…"

And after a leisurely but somewhat pensive sip of brandy, he added, "If your target appliance customers, like GE and Miele, or ADT and Securitas AB, or all the other suppliers for home electronics think like real businessmen, then I believe that they will like it too. It does not require them to spend a lot of up-front money. That is always good. Plus this whole AI twist would give them an excuse to increase their prices. That is good for them, since it is opposite to the usual trend—normally maturing markets drive price reduction. So I suspect that they will jump on it. Yes, I like it. I think that you can sell this to your prospective customers, and even to other investors…"

We then got into a lively discussion trading questions and answers, ideas and concepts, elaborations and suggestions.

Tigran mentioned that if we did develop the software in Armenia, or for that matter anywhere in Eastern Europe, he might be able to throw in some extra money to accelerate the effort ahead of Round-A. "A relatively low investment might reduce overall time to money. And that is bound to pull in more investors."

Aram kept refilling our glasses.

However you turned it, we seemed to have our business plan!

Around midnight Stiglitz blurted out, "The company name is perfect!" Not normally a drinking man, his complexion glowed a nice shade of pink. "Not only for the cute tagline, but it means 'clean,' doesn't it? Very appropriate since if we use an Eastern European software partner, we could be in the cleaning business…"

"What do you mean?" I asked. His comment did not make sense and somehow caught me off guard.

Tigran rapped on the table with his ring to attract Stiglitz's attention, a new habit that reminded me of Frank Underwood from the *House of Cards* series, and then gave him a hard stare.

Stiglitz caught Tigran's look, might have paled a bit, and then shook himself awake and blurted, "Never mind. I've said too much. I'm talking nonsense. Just forget it."

But I could not just 'forget it.' Stiglitz's comment was like a worm that burrowed into my mind. What had he meant by 'cleaning business?' It brought back all the worries that I'd had previously that I let go.

However, the reference nagged at me throughout the long weekend. Bev noticed that I was distracted and asked about it, but I just waved it off. No point worrying her.

The day after Labor Day we were back to normal. Tigran had gone back to Armenia, or wherever he went, and it was just the three of us again. I asked Stiglitz if he wanted to go for an after-lunch walk. We sometimes did that when the weather was nice. When we were alone, I confronted him again and asked what he meant by the 'cleaning' comment. He blushed and muttered something about having had too much to drink. I pressed him again and he then turned quite serious and said, "Look, Professor, I said too much. I was drunk. I should not have spoken. Please, don't bring it up again." And he abruptly turned and walked back in the direction of the business park. I was dumbfounded, and certainly not reassured.

Later that afternoon I cornered Aram in his office and asked him what he'd thought of Stiglitz's comment.

"Professor, you worry about nothing," he shrugged. "Since the beginning you've been nagging me that we need a full and complete Business Plan. Well, I believe we now have one. So, let's raise the capital to actually execute it. Let's build that pitch, go on the road, and raise the money instead of worrying about ghosts and innuendo."

"But what if Tigran is funding us with illicit money, and using Mak'Ur to launder it?"

Once expressed in explicit language, the possibility worried me even more. Perhaps it was the Serbian in me always looking for a conspiracy or a scam. Or perhaps it was all the stories of money laundering rampant in Montenegro and the rest of the Balkans. Or maybe it was a result of the bias in the media that automatically associated illegal activities with anyone tagged as an 'oligarch.'

"Professor, you are always looking for the turd in the punch-bowl," Aram responded. "Besides, when we attract additional investors their due diligence will reveal anything illegal or improper. Come to think of it, surely Tigran is not stupid enough to use dirty money to support us going through Series-A funding and risk being discovered. So, don't worry. There is nothing there. Let's focus and go for that Round-A. We have all worked too hard to get here. So, c'mon!"

I had no answer to that. What he said was not irrational. But the worry nagged at me. After all, what did we know about Tigran and the source of our funding. Nothing, really. And Tigran had insisted that we not ask. Was he in fact using dirty money?

Perhaps for the lack of an alternative I decided to do exactly as Aram had suggested. I would rely on the professionals—the VCs to do full and proper due diligence as a way of assuring myself that we were clean and not complicit in anything unethical.

ROUND-A

The next few months were all about Round-A., building our business plan, massaging our presentation and orchestrating meetings with potential investors. I put my network in overdrive and was on the phone 24-7, leveraging all my connections and pulling every string that I possibly could to get in front of some of the VCs in Silicon Valley. This was obviously critical for Mak'Ur and I felt that the onus was on me to make it happen. I knew that this was part of the reason that Aram and Tigran had insisted on me being part of the company, so I felt that I had to deliver to prove my worth and to fulfill and justify my role.

In the middle of that frenzy Tigran called. A direct call to me, not through Stiglitz! I was surprised—shocked even—as this had never happened before. But he was pleasant and said that there were some associates of his who might be interested to invest and would I please get in touch with them. He gave me three names and corresponding contact information: Herr Shraffzigger in Germany, Sheikh Sharavi in Dubai, and Hashimoto-san in Japan.

After we hung up, I sat in my office for quite a while in a kind of a daze and just stared out a window. My version of shellshock, I suppose. Tigran—our unorthodox Angel—had not only invested seed money but was now bringing on investors for Round-A.

In view of the concerns that were already fomenting in the back of my mind, I imagined various sinister reasons for his call. Was this a way to circumvent the standard VC due diligence? During some of my more out-of-control moments I had visions of our Board of Directors consisting of all sorts of ugly thugs and goons—faces straight out of the Rogues Gallery.

After a day or two I calmed down and parsed it all in my head. My reaction was mostly a consequence of a surprise, probably because his direct call was unexpected. Nevertheless, I conceded that there was nothing wrong with Tigran trying to leverage some of his connections to attract other money. It was simply a way of protecting his investment.

I also realized that part of the reason for my anxiety was because I was not sure how to deal with these so-called 'associates' of his. I knew how to approach VCs, but was not sure about some who-knew-what in Dubai? I confess that I was a bit scared, and my imagination was beginning to run wild. But after some Google searches on the names that Tigran had given me, I came to understand—perhaps because it was convenient for me—that these men were probably just regular business people looking for a hot deal. I found references on the web on two out of the three of them and it appeared that they were second tier celebs by virtue of their wealth. The man in Germany, apparently a manufacturer of rivets, screws and other hardware, was mentioned in the context of a contentious divorce a few years ago; and the man in Dubai was apparently in the construction business and came up as part of a government contract in Iraq. I could not find anything on the Japanese contact.

As far as I could tell they were not gangsters, or notorious Russian oligarchs, or front men for North Korean illicit businesses, or ogres or aliens. After calming down I called each in turn, and the experience proved to be anticlimactic because all they wanted to do was put me in touch with their private secretaries who were instructed to find suitable openings on their calendars.

So, all three of us hopped a plane and went to meet with them. To say that they were interesting meetings would be an understatement. They were fascinating and unforgettable—especially from a personal point of view. In terms of business, they were routine, mostly because the outcome was predestined, and certainly not as exciting as some of the meetings with real VCs where I felt the outcome might hang on a right choice of a single word. Nevertheless, these guys were a source of real money, and as such extremely important to us. As Aram confirmed,

"Who cares who they are and why they invest; all that matters is the money!"

As it turned out, all three were similar: self-made men with big egos—perhaps deservedly so—who knew nothing about technology but who had money they could afford to lose—money, apparently, that they had set aside for a long shot bet. The way one of them put it was "a roll of the dice on one of those Silicon Valley startups where dollars become millions overnight. Like magic." The sense I got was that at least a part of their interest was not so much the money but also the bump to their reputations. Apparently, in their circles there was more sex appeal in investment in technology than investments in mundane things like rivets or construction or convenience stores.

But it was also money that they did not intend to lose—after all, they were not stupid men, and they had their constraints and considerations, none of which had to do with technology or anything that I could talk to them about. From their point of view the purpose of the meeting that we flew halfway around the world to attend was so that they could look us in the eye and assure themselves that we did exist and were for real, so that they could do a bit of grand standing, and so that they could dictate their conditions. It was remarkable how similar their thinking was, despite being so very different in terms of culture, age, temperament and background. All three seemed to have two deal-breaker kind of constraints: one was that they would be willing to invest only if Tigran did as well (evidently Tigran had a reputation for making his investments work); and secondly that they would invest only if we could find a real Silicon Valley VC who would lead the round. Apparently that was their way of assuring themselves that what we said really made technical sense.

The meetings themselves were extremely memorable—perhaps set up to be so. Then again, I am not sure that we rated high enough to merit a special event on their calendars. An early evening meeting followed by drinks and fancy snacks seemed to be the norm, regardless whether it was in a private villa overlooking Elbe with Herr Shraffzigger, a yacht moored at Dubai marina with Sheikh Sharavi, or a penthouse with a view of Shinjuku in

Tokyo with Hashimoto-san. Stunningly beautiful 'assistants'—aka waitresses—subtly managed to imply that they were offering more than just drinks and snacks. "*Anything* else, sir?"

Perhaps I'd seen too many movies and was viewing the world through a Hollywood prism. Or perhaps it was just a glimpse into the regular lives of the rich and famous. Who knows?

Long story short, the upshot of these meetings was that we had to find a knowledgeable and credible professional venture capitalist with a proven track record in technology investments—the kind that the Silicon Valley is famous for—who would be willing to be the lead investor and who could convince these guys to throw in their chump change with him. The good news was that we needed only one VC since these associates of Tigran's were willing to top up the pot.

And I did...

One of my doctoral students from back in the days when my lab at the university was churning out superstars was involved with several startups on the West Coast and had become a part of Silicon Valley fabric, so to speak. He did what was expected of a successful technology entrepreneur: moved up to a big house in the Santa Cruz mountains overlooking the Valley and picked up trendy hobbies such as breeding some specialty kind of chicken in his backyard and running a winery somewhere in Marin County. Anyway, this ex-student had become an industry personality who'd joined the speakers' circuit and often gave interviews and opinions to the trade press. So I called him, we talked and reminisced, and he finally put me in touch with Luigi Lorenzo, a VC who had backed some of his ventures.

Luigi was also a known veteran of the industry—an Italian technologist who had been transplanted to the Bay Area through some acquisition or other, and who ended up at the top of the management ladder of some sexy company that was sold for megabucks back in the go-go days of the '90s. He apparently made a lot of money in that transaction and then used it to start a private venture fund. And since then his VC firm had been associated with several successful technology startups, thereby growing his investment pot. He was not one of the major VCs—not on the annual Forbes Midas List, where returns of the order of billions of dollars were the ante. But he was an investor who specialized in specific types of technology startups and had a pretty good track record.

He was also a regular on the speakers' circuit offering opinions on industry trends and such. There were several of those in Silicon Valley—boutique firms known to the insiders and headed by some smart ex-engineer who liked to keep his fingers in the industry pie. It seemed that other than breeding chickens or running wineries, becoming a VC was not an unusual way for successful technologists to retire. Luigi was one of those. He had a reputation for being very selective, but once he invested in a venture, then he liked to be hands-on, involved, and connected all the way up to a profitable exit. Often his involvement continued even beyond that point because some of the companies that he'd spun out retained him on their Board of Directors, presumably valuing his wisdom and experience. The Bay Area gossip queens loved him—reminding me of the regular denizens of small-town cafés back in Montenegro, who knew everything worth knowing about anything that was going on, and who were not shy to spend their entire days sharing it authoritatively and with a conviction of people who held the secret truth.

Anyway, Luigi Lorenzo had quite a reputation in the Valley for his investments, for his involvement with external ventures, and for his ways and hobbies.

Perfect for us, I thought, a boutique firm, technically competent and colorful enough to impress Tigran's 'associates.' I called him, and true to his Italian roots he was not a man of few words. But we resonated, technologist to technologist, so I set up a meeting.

This turned out to be another very memorable experience…

Luigi was a bit of a character and seemed to enjoy—even nurture—his reputation as an old school Italian style banker. Maybe he fancied himself to be a descendent of the House of Medici? He gave an impression that he would have liked to be referred to as *Don* Lorenzo, and even looked the part, favoring double-breasted pin stripe suits—a very un-Silicon Valley look—and speaking with affectations that belied his thirty years in America. We met in the conference room of his office suite.

It had the look and feel of a library in some old villa, with walls lined with shelves filled with big dusty leather-bound tomes. The entire office suite was however infused with the smell of coffee, along with the noise that came from an Italian café one floor below. Some contrast, I thought, a high-tech VC office above a street café. And the fact that it was on the main street in the old part of Palo Alto, just a mile or so from Stanford University—the veritable Kaaba of the high-tech world—only served to amplify the contrasts. But that was all just the front. Luigi was sharp as a stiletto, technically very competent and clearly quite savvy about the business world.

All three of us—Aram, Stiglitz and I—came for the audience. It was clear that if we could get Luigi to lead the investment round, we would be set. We went through our standard presentation, which was by then quite polished and which we could probably recite in our sleep. Aram talked the company and the business plan, I did the technology and the market, and Stiglitz walked through the projected cost and revenue numbers. His last slide was a copy of the letters of credit from the bankers of Tigran's 'associates.'

Luigi was an interactive audience who peppered us with questions and comments for just about every bullet point on every slide. But what really seemed to catch his attention were those letters of credit. He wanted to know everything that we knew and even took notes. At the time I felt that this was somewhat demoralizing. Here we were talking about our great technology, excellent ideas, and awesome business strategy, but the thing that he wanted to know was the backgrounds of the other potential investors, where their money came from, and how much each was worth.

I guess from his perspective that made sense. He was technically competent and probably understood the technology and the associated value propositions instantly. He had been around the block and could readily understand the business plan and all its nuances. So he could weigh the business and technology risks associated with Mak'Ur almost intuitively. But from his perspective, the unknown variable—the real risk to him in this proposition—was the money that the others were kicking in.

In fact, they were putting up millions, whereas at that point the value of Mak'Ur may have been in the hundreds of thousands. And these men were unknown to him—not like other Bay Area VCs with whom he'd worked. He must have asked himself the question: If those investors were to pull out, would he be left holding the bag?

Luigi was also excited about a possibility of access to third party money for this project, and possibly for other future technology investments. Having others—especially from outside the Silicon Valley circle—contribute money to his technology investment pool would give him a multiplying factor. Surely a good thing for him. So, no wonder he was interested in them...

We spent the entire day with him answering any question that we could, and generally getting to know each other. Afterward, we walked down the street to an Italian restaurant where he ordered a proper dinner: *Aperitivo, Antipasto, Primo, Secondo, Insalata, Formaggi e frutta, Dolce, Digestivo con caffè...* Oof! And all throughout the feast he talked about his one and true love: the 1935 Alfa Romeo 8C that he was showing at the Pebble Beach Concours d'Elegance. I later found out that the real contestants for the prized Best of Show award were typically valued around five million dollars—clearly, not a cheap hobby.

At the end of the evening we shook hands: we had a deal— subject to due diligence, of course.

The next month or so involved little else other than responding to Luigi's requests for all sorts of paperwork, data, commitments, and plans, which was apparently a standard part of his due diligence. Stiglitz bore the brunt of it, and in an off-moment said that he felt like he'd had a proctology exam, "by a slow and thorough doctor with very fat fingers," he added. This was as funny and open as Stiglitz ever got, so I presume it really did get to him. But Stiglitz had spent the past year getting ready for something like this, so I knew he could handle it. With Mak'Ur in such early stages of development, and with just the three... well, five... of us, it was not so much a matter of accounting for money spent—there wasn't that much of that really—it was more a matter of convincing Luigi that our infrastructure and financial practices were up to par. From what I could gather from Stiglitz, the hardest part was the review of the books for our Yerevan office. But Stiglitz cleverly ascribed the problems purely to the differences in the accounting practices between Armenia and the US.

We were not involved in Luigi's due diligence on his fellow investors. Stiglitz—via Tigran—put him in touch with their finance people, and whatever exchanges may or may not have occurred, took place directly between Luigi and the other investors, and did not involve Mak'Ur. Presumably the same exchange took place between Luigi and Tigran or Tigran's people. But Luigi did let it drop that having ready made investors lined up and primed made things easier, and that we were in fact on a very fast track. In the end, Luigi seemed to be satisfied that the financial side of things looked good.

I was of course relieved to see a positive review; because surely, Luigi's due diligence would have uncovered any impropriety in our funding if there were any to be found. This should have allayed the worries and concerns that kept resurfacing in my thoughts, but it did not—at least not completely.

Then Luigi turned his attention to the market assessment and insisted on going over our study point by point. I was so glad that from the start Aram had made us document everything, and he buried poor Luigi in paperwork—all those trip reports and assessment reports and post-meeting notes. He then wanted to talk with a target teaching client or two, and I put him in touch with Elvira. I don't know if he actually called her, and if so, what they talked about, but whatever happened, the outcome seemed to be favorable. I never heard anything on the topic from either of them.

For Aram and me the best part was responding to Luigi's questions in the technical domain. He was sharp and in fact his questions helped us to clarify some loose ends. By the middle of December he was done. Everything was in order. As a result, we received a commitment for fifty-six million dollars! Twenty million dollars from Luigi, ten million each from Tigran's associates, and the balance from Tigran himself—or more precisely from the offshore shell companies that Stiglitz told us were Tigran's front.

Round-A funding was guaranteed. What a Christmas present!

In some crazy, wacky moment—I must have been giddy from celebrating too much—I figured out that stacking fifty-six million one-dollar bills would produce a pile about 5.6 kilometers high and would weigh some fifty-six tons!

We even convened the official Board of Directors for Mak'Ur AI, Inc. Comprising of the three founders with Stiglitz acting on Tigran's behalf, Luigi as the chair, and one seat that was intended to cycle between the three independent investors which for the moment went to the representative of Herr Shraffzigger. One additional seat was to be reserved for an independent external Director. The first items that the BoD discussed was the suitable candidates for that independent member. I suggested Elvira. Luigi immediately saw the value of having a potential lead client on the Board and readily seconded the nomination.

I tentatively floated the offer to her, suspecting that the position could be a conflict of interest since the plan was for the two companies to do business together, but she corrected me and said that the intent was to collaborate—as opposed to simply doing business—and as such it should not be a problem. It took her only a couple of weeks to get the approval of her own Board, and to formally accept the seat. The downside, of course, was that I just knew that at some point in time I would slip and call her "Elvira" rather than "Barbara" or "Dr.Vasquez." Nevertheless, we had completed our Board of Directors!

Luigi joked that we had just acquired a new mother-in-law—namely him—since he intended to be as intrusive as any mother-in-law would be. He even suggested that we should move to the Bay Area because we would not be taken seriously by the supply chain and would have harder time attracting real talent, if we were to continue operating from the East Coast. But I suspected that he wanted us to relocate so that he could keep a better eye on us. Like a good mother-in-law...

CIRCA 2019:
SERIES B ROUND

Growing the Company

It did not take us long to realize that Luigi was right. Once we got the Round-A funding, it was all about growing the company and hiring. We could easily attract new grads and young engineers, especially from our Alma Mater, but hiring experienced and competent engineers was a different matter. At the stage of development that Mak'Ur was at, our key challenge was to attract the Chiefs as well as the Indians: lead designers and architects, senior technologists, section and middle level managers, vice presidents; heavy weight professionals who would shape the company and the product. Without those we could not use the 'hands' to do the detailed engineering. Similarly, we needed business and program managers, silicon supply chain managers, product managers and sales specialists—at least a skeleton staff of the professional support required to source a real electronics product. All were found relatively easily in the Bay Area; on the East Coast, not so much.

Young engineers typically do not have families and may not own a home, and as such they move to wherever they can find the best job—especially with the name recognition that I thought I still enjoyed. On the other hand, senior people—specifically, the experienced professionals—already had good jobs and were typically tied down with family obligations, mortgages, and a network of friends and colleagues, and were therefore reluctant to move. Like it or not, the concentration of skill sets that we needed were located in the Silicon Valley. Some in the Northwest, some in Austin, some in North Carolina, but the Bay Area was still very much the center.

In addition, the rest of the vital infrastructure for developing, designing, and verifying an advanced technology product was also based in the Silicon Valley: providers of design tools and building blocks, reps for manufacturing and assembly services, Test and Characterization Labs, Thermal and Mechanical consultants were all readily available in the Bay Area, both in terms of physical proximity and network connections. Not so much on the East Coast.

So, Luigi was right. It became clear that we needed a presence in the Bay Area if we were to hire the talent that we had to have in order to build the company in the kind of timeframe that we had in mind.

We entertained the idea of possibly bypassing the problem by outsourcing some—or even all—of the silicon design, and focusing in-house only on the final assembly and packaging. So we looked into design services companies, both in the US—again mostly based in the Bay Area—and also abroad. But in the end, Aram rejected the idea on principle. "If we outsource hardware design, we outsource our soul," he insisted. "That may be okay for someone who already has brand value in the market—those 'lick and stick' kind of companies, but not for us. If we outsource hardware design, we are nothing but an empty shell, and we have no future—especially since the plan is for most of our revenue and market differentiation to be derived from hardware." That was that, regardless how good some of the engineering services companies may have been.

The software side was a bit easier for us—or so we thought at the time. Software was meant to be our foot-in-the-door, and our strategic intent was to leverage the best-in-class of all the specialty software packages that could be licensed commercially; such as face and voice recognition, training algorithms and data bases. We certainly did not intend to re-invent those wheels, or try to be the best AI software point-tool maker. No, we did not even intend to particularly differentiate Mak'Ur through the integration architecture other than being the first in the smart home market and possibly having a slick customized wrapper. So we felt that all we needed was some code to integrate the commercial packages and to interface with the target appliances, which could be written anywhere, including

Eastern Europe. All we needed on-site was a few high-level architects to define the spec and possibly some Software QA to validate the code. And even those few software architects that we wanted in-house were more readily found in the Bay Area rather than the East Coast.

This posed quite a problem for me. Aram and Stiglitz were young, single and free and prepared to move to the moon if necessary. But for me such a decision was more difficult. I approached Bev and felt her out on the idea of moving. She left no doubt that there was no way in hell that she would move to the West Coast. Her job, her career and her friends and family were on the East Coast.

"No! No way, no how. This was not a part of the deal," she insisted. "I cannot, and will not, drop everything and move. I am not, never will be, nor want to ever be a 'California girl!'"

It was clear that there was no point in arguing, and, frankly, I fully understood her resistance. I must admit, I was not so keen on the idea of moving either.

On the other hand, somebody had to go. I knew this even before I went to confront Aram. I am not sure what I expected him to do, but I felt like I was in a jam, and for once, I needed to vent.

So, during one of our usual late-night sessions over pizza, Aram, Stiglitz and I had a long discussion to address the core problem that was staring us in the face. "Yes, Professor, understood," Aram said in response to my concerns about hiring challenges and how all the good candidates seemed to be in the Bay Area, and how I was tired of flying to the West Coast to interview them, only to have our offers turned down... "Right now," he continued, "our problem is hiring talent. And the talent is on the West Coast. Muhammad must go to the mountain."

I said something about not wanting to be the Muhammad that went to that particular mountain, and that my Aisha, i.e. Bev, would absolutely not move, and that I was tired of travelling, and that...

"Yes, Professor, I understand," Aram responded in as soothing a tone as he could manage. "But need I remind you, the corporate plan that was funded has us co-developing software and hardware in parallel. So, for the next year or so, it is clear that the company needs one of us facing west, as in the Silicon Valley for hardware design, and one of us to face east, as in Eastern Europe for Software development. That much is clear to me. There is no other way that I can see."

A pregnant silence followed, making the absence of any constructive or even plausible suggestions blatantly obvious. He then posed a definitive question: "So, Professor, which would you prefer?"

Stiglitz piped in, "Not that it is up to me, but I vote for the professor facing west."

"Why?" I turned on Stiglitz, probably mostly because I wanted to argue with anyone and everyone to vent my frustration.

"Because," he reacted defensively, "I think that the company would benefit more from you dealing with hardware. It is your bailiwick, and your name would be a positive asset in the hardware domain. And for the other, Tigran thought that Aram's Armenian origins would be more of an asset in dealing with a software team in Yerevan."

"And my Serbian name would be a liability?" I shot back.

It did not occur to me then to question why Tigran would have an opinion on the matter. Normally he did not interfere in those kinds of decisions, so why would he want to keep me out of Armenia? At the time I let it go, much as I had with so many issues on so many other occasions. Surely, I liked the way the company was growing—it was everything that we'd envisioned—but I did not like some of the consequences, and certainly did not want to move to the Bay Area.

"In the end, that's up to you," Aram broke in, "but I tend to agree with Stiglitz. C'mon, Professor, would you rather fly to Yerevan? And whether you move or choose to live on an airplane is also up to you. But the company needs you to take on one of those two roles."

And that more or less settled it. I was to be the lead on the hardware design and the associated hiring on the West Coast, and Aram would take care of the software business in Armenia or elsewhere in Eastern Europe. And Stiglitz would remain at our headquarters to hold down the fort.

West Coast
Design Center

My plan was to hire an experienced executive as soon as possible, and to rely on him or her to take care of most of the local business. The intent was to open a design center somewhere in the Bay Area and hopefully to have it run more or less autonomously. Therefore my physical presence would be required maybe once a month or so.

Well, that was the plan…

Thanks to all the headhunters in the Bay Area we did find several excellent candidates to fill in that local executive slot. In the end, we hired a Dr. Peter Kibarian. He was clearly also of Armenian origin but that was purely coincidental in the sense that we did not actively seek to hire an Armenian; but it may not have been coincidental in the sense that he might have looked favorably upon a company with an Armenian logo, a CEO who had an Armenian name, and which had a design center in Yerevan.

In fact, Peter K. was from LA, a second generation Russian-Armenian, a graduate of UCLA and Berkley, and a veteran of quite a few companies in the Silicon Valley: Intel; Cadence; Mentor; Apple. *That* was an asset we sought, local roots with local connections, to hopefully accelerate our hiring. Ultimately Silicon Valley worked by word of mouth. The presence of all the high-tech companies in the area enabled a very fluid and mobile engineering workforce. In Silicon Valley it was a standard joke that you could change your job without changing your carpool. So having a man who had been around in the area was definitely an asset. He very likely knew a so-and-so who was very good at such-and-such from working together at this or that company... This worked right down the line so that, once assembled, each member of the team had some prior personal and/or professional connectivity with at least one other member.

The net result was that we managed to assemble a complete team, including the usual office and support staff, in record time—only a couple of quarters. An unintended side effect was that we ended up with a design center where a substantial number of employees were Armenian or Russian. English was obviously the business language, but Armenian and Russian could often be heard in corridor conversations at Mak'Ur AI, Inc.

Perhaps if our seed hire, Peter Kibarian, had been Indian or Chinese, we might have ended up with a different ethnic mix using Hindi or Mandarin as second languages, and the office atmosphere might also have been different. Who knows?

Mind you, in a gossip-fueled community like the Valley, the fact that we were a hot startup in a sexy arena that had been recently funded to the tune of fifty-six million dollars, and that the round was led by a Luigi Lorenzo, did not hurt at all. Rumors that we had received oil money from Abu Dhabi also helped. My name might have helped a bit, too, but maybe that was mostly in my head.

We opened a design center in downtown San Jose, rather than in any of the more prestigious communities further north along Route 101 which seemed to be the backbone of Silicon Valley. So we avoided places such as Sunnyvale, Mountainview, Palo Alto, Menlo Park, Redwood, and others and instead chose San Jose, partially because it was cheaper (the closer to San Francisco the more expensive the real estate), and partially because most of our lead hires lived further north and preferred to commute against the traffic. And, I confess, partially because I preferred the urban feel of downtown San Jose, as opposed to the warehouse feel in those sprawling suburban communities. To someone born and bred in Europe and accustomed to living on the urbanized East Coast of the United States, amenities such as sidewalks with streetlights and a choice of restaurants within walking distance mattered. I could get that in downtown San Jose.

The work at the design center ramped up very nicely, and the capability, performance and morale of the team seemed to be excellent. Peter K.—the EVP responsible for leading the project and managing the site—did an outstanding job. He focused on the technical deliverables and delegated the mechanics of the day-to-day running of the site to the office manager (more like our official office goddess). She—Irena— was a beautiful Russian woman who managed the place using a bizarre mixture of Russian proverbs and English idioms. She seemed to have everybody eating out of her hand using her unique combination of carrots and sticks. From what I could see her 'carrot' was liberal use of flirtatious womanly charms. I am sure that she thought that I was a bit slow, because she had to explain to me that Armenian men liked beautiful blonde Russian ladies (apparently a known and verifiable fact) and that it was her job to keep them happy, and happy engineers were productive engineers. And her 'stick' was either threatening or sometimes actually booking the middle seat on a transoceanic flight for the unlucky miscreant who merited punishment. Not quite PC, but it seemed to work, and from what I could see everybody loved her, and dutifully showered her with all kinds of gifts. In return she took care of all office chores, boosted the team spirit, kept the place well supplied with treats, provided laughs and entertainment, managed the travel, organized all sorts of team building activities, and controlled a secret supply of 'under the table' Armenian brandy. I suspect that the Russian/Armenian engineers enjoyed it and thought that it was the norm, and that the non-Russian/Armenian engineers found it so unusual that it was refreshing for them. Either way, the design center was humming away, so I turned a blind eye to her antics. A bit reminiscent of Joan Harris from the *Mad Men* TV series—except that that was fiction and set in the '60s and this was reality set in the #MeToo era. But, why mess with success? Strictly speaking, it was Peter K.'s problem, and I knew better than to micromanage.

All that went to plan. As for the part about me travelling only once a month? Well, not so much…

I was now spending half my time on the West Coast, so I

moved semi-permanently into that handy little apartment that Stiglitz had found. It turned out that many activities required a personal, face-to-face touch. First, it had been to establish the design center, to hire the talent, to deploy the infrastructure, to negotiate all the support contracts, to... And then it was to set up relationships with the foundries, to obtain the design kits, to put together procurement agreements for the standard chiplets, to find a willing and capable assembly house, to... And then it was to see and be seen dealing with the specific product design questions and tradeoffs... All managed so much easier through face-to-face interactions as opposed to phone or video calls, or e-mails.

In fact, I had started to nag Stiglitz about finding a bigger apartment within walking distance of the office—partially because the old one was a bit cramped for my extended stays, and partially because we were ramping up an exchange program with our Yerevan office, and the Armenian engineers could use it, too. Much cheaper and much nicer than having them stay at hotels.

In addition, my international travel had not exactly wound down. The accepted convention was that the relationships with the supply chain partners were set up top-down and in face-to-face meetings—especially so for the Asian suppliers. So, as 'the front' for Mak'Ur AI hardware activities, and as its CTO, I was expected to schmooze with my counterparts—the usual C-Level Suite denizens—at least to kick off the relationships and establish an understanding. The details could then be worked out via phone or video calls at other suitable organizational levels. That was how it was done, or so I was told. Hence, relatively frequent trips to China, Taiwan, Korea, and Japan were necessary.

Fortunately, the company policy was changed to support business class travel, which made for an entirely different flying experience. Aram insisted that we should have a corporate travel policy, and Stiglitz worked up the numbers and indicated that paying for business class for every trip for every employee would be prohibitively expensive, and probably questionable in front of our investors, so we had a debate about the right criteria for corporate business class travel. Traveler's size or weight, the length of a trip, flight frequency or duration, travelers rank or age, and so forth. Personally, I favored travelers' age as the right critical parameter knowing that I was still the oldest man in the company. Stiglitz argued that business class should be a perk reserved for senior management only. Either way, I ended up qualifying for the upgrade and took full advantage of it. Flying became a downright enjoyable experience.

Another aspect of travel to Asia was that building those relationships involved wining and dining of visiting dignitaries. That would be me. And this was not limited to excessive eating and drinking in the best local restaurants, which I did enjoy. Other relationship-building activities were also frequently proposed; such as visits to private resorts with exotic spas, excursions to theaters or to other cultural venues, or the best in local entertainment, which sometimes included massages and even 'female companionship.' I never accepted any of the more adventurous offers, not being the kind of a man who, even when young, got a kick out of one-night stands. Let alone now, as an older man who was loyal to his wife, and frankly, who prized a good night's sleep more than a roll in the hay with some young girl. I did struggle with how to refuse those offers without being offensive or appearing judgmental. Sometimes this resulted in our hosts offering male companionship, instead. But I think that was mostly to impress the westerners with their modern and progressive views. Or maybe they had their doubts about my orientation. After all, what other reason could there be for turning down female companionship?

Still, spending so much time away from home was a pain in the ass, and I especially resented the inevitable distancing between Bev and me. It seemed that for the two of us the saying 'out of sight out of mind' applied more than 'absence makes the heart grow fonder.' The way things worked between us, we both always had our independence, what with our respective careers, but the protracted absence did have a chilling effect on our relationship. On occasion we still took weekend trips, and we made sure to carve out our 'together time' when I was home. But there was a new sense of remoteness between us that bothered me—nothing like open war or talk of separation or divorce—but there was definitely a chill in the air. But I had no choice and hoped that it would not last too long.

The part that I actually did like about spending so much time in the Bay Area was the networking. Being a CTO of a startup that was successfully funded brought with it a certain notoriety. I became 'the face' of a cool company that everybody wanted to hear from. Between Luigi introducing me around, me reconnecting with my various ex-students who had settled in the Silicon Valley, various academics and acquaintances from my past reaching out, and all my new business contacts, I was busy. And popular! Just like the glory days of my academic career when I was the hot shot researcher on the conference circuit. But better. Because this time around it was more than just giving interviews to the industry rags, or being on discussion panels at various conferences. This time not only did people want to hear what I had to say, but I was also wined and dined, and I was able to rub shoulders with some iconic people in our industry. This time I had an expense account, and was a frequent guest of other people who had expense accounts. And, I guess I found out that in contrast to being the professor that needed funding, I was now on the receiving rather than the giving end of what often felt like a veritable butt-kissing-fest. My butt was 'virgin' as far as that practice was concerned, but I enjoyed the novelty of the experience. So I admit; my newfound role felt good. What can I say? I liked being in demand.

EAST EUROPE
DESIGN CENTER

At that time we also had to relocate our offices. The fact that we were now a funded and established company violated the terms of our lease agreement at the incubator business center, so we were obliged to move. But, partially to comply with the government regulations, and partially because the company now needed a physical location to house its servers and paperwork, and ultimately because we needed an established contact point, we had to have a permanent address for World Headquarters of Mak'Ur AI, Inc. How pretentious does that sound?

Stiglitz did his magic, and after the usual debate we agreed to relocate just a few blocks down the road from our previous address, mostly because the three of us were not yet ready to make a commitment about a more permanent move. So we rented a suitable suite that included several prestigious-looking offices, a conference room, a separate coffee area/kitchenette, and even a private lobby with a big logo over the reception desk. It all looked like a real company, rather than just a figment of our imaginations. We even hired a permanent administrative assistant to work the reception area, and a CPA to help Stiglitz. So our headquarters were expanded and upgraded but the circumstances were such that they were barely used. I got to use my fancy corner office only when I was not on the road or not on the West Coast. Aram got busy with the activities in Eastern Europe, so he used his office only when he was in the States. Stiglitz ended up being the real beneficiary of our prestigious location, as he remained local most of the time.

Yes, Aram was spending much of his time in Eastern Europe,

specifically in Armenia. He realized that the most effective way to deliver on our ambitious software plans was to assemble a dedicated team. Apparently there were plenty of software service companies—some very good, some just so-so—both in Armenia and elsewhere in Eastern Europe; but after dealing with some of them he came to a conclusion that using any software service company would involve inevitable inefficiencies. He realized that this was intrinsic to the services business model, rather than being a function of a specific company or the nature of a contract, so he concluded that we had to hire our own software engineers.

Then, apparently acting on a suggestion from Tigran, they acquired one of the service companies—CodeWriter, LLC—in Yerevan. This seemed like the fastest way to hire fifty pre-trained software engineers, and Tigran had a connection to this particular one, as well as a preference for keeping the business in Armenia.

Legally, the acquisition required approval of the Board of Directors, and we hastily called a special online meeting to review the opportunity. The entire transaction was expeditiously approved as it seemed like the fastest way of assembling a team. It accelerated company growth and shortened time-to-money, and given the cost of labor in Armenia, it offered an excellent return on the investment when this was calculated based on US cost structure.

At the time it did not occur to me to question why Tigran might have an opinion on how or where we staffed the operation, or how come he, a self-confessed technology outsider, had a preference for one software company over another. To me it seemed odd, but this was Aram's responsibility and most of it came to me second hand and after the fact.

However it was done, the Yerevan design center ballooned from its original two employees. Mak'Ur AI, Inc. (Armenia), now occupied two floors in a modern building, only a stone's throw away from the university, which seemed to be the right address for housing a local hi-tech company.

At the next full Board of Directors meeting Stiglitz presented a review of the entire transaction. This BoD meeting was in-person and combined with our annual shareholders meeting, which we had to have in order to comply with the SEC rules. Apparently, the net cost to the company was just $6.5M, including the acquisition of CodeWriter LLC, their relocation, and the rent for our new office space. This was very good for a fully functioning software center with more than fifty engineers. He also droned on about various transactional costs, exchange rates, and local and international banking rules, but my attention drifted.

The part that interested me was Aram's report, which stated that the software side of the enterprise was on track, and that the beta release of both the software backbone and the Mak'Ur AI App was on plan, and the initial on-site QA evaluations and the pilot field testing at Elvira Inc. were scheduled and primed to go. His assessment seemed more than good. We had pulled ourselves up by our bootstraps and obtained a complete software team in a single swoop, and we were well on our way toward product introduction.

In a private moment after the BoD meeting Aram pulled me aside and muttered in mock anger, "Damn it, Professor, you and your Elvira tag. It's now hard-wired in my head, and I came very close to slipping in there... Almost called Barbara 'Elvira' to her face. And how do you explain that she is the CEO of Elvira, Inc. without coming off as some kind of a chauvinist?" We had a good laugh over that.

That particular Board Meeting was held at our San Jose office, so after we finished the serious business, I organized a wrap-up at the Plumed Horse Restaurant, a swanky establishment about ten miles from the office that just happened to have a couple of Michelin stars. By guidebook definition this was 'a restaurant worth a detour, indicating excellent cuisine and skillfully and carefully crafted dishes of outstanding quality.' Even Luigi approved despite it not being an Italian restaurant, and *Herr* Shraffzigger seemed quite happy too, although I am sure that he was no stranger to fine dining. That dinner was definitely a checkmark on my Fat Cat resume.

Yes, everything seemed to be on track!

A Fly in the Ointment

It all started with a stupid rumor. I happened to overhear a conversation between some of our local staff and one of the visiting Armenians, and it drew my attention because it was quite lively and accompanied by animated hand gestures and excited faces. Judging by the number of heads peering over cubicle partitions and listening, it clearly drew the attention of a few other people as well. The exchange was in Armenian, so I did not understand a word of it, and in passing I asked Irina, the Russian office manager, what it was about. She flashed her baby blues and assured me earnestly that she would let me know. I had no doubt that she would find out, and I duly forgot all about it.

A day or so later, she came to my office, closed the door, and leaned across my desk and said that she knew that it is not fair and that the people would be unhappy, and that... My befuddled expression must have been convincing, probably confirming her opinion that I was a bit slow, and she proceeded to explain. Apparently, the employees in Armenia had just received a large bonus equal to two month's pay. Irina assured me that this was indeed the case as she had confirmed it with her counterpart in the Yerevan office, and she demanded to know why the employees in San Jose had not been treated equally. She explained that people in California worked just as hard and that it was not fair, and that some were upset. She all but demanded that I somehow address this gross injustice.

So I called Aram, and asked him. He explained that extra money was indeed granted to some of the Yerevan employees, but said that (a) this was a part of a sign-on bonus package for the CodeWriter transferees, and (b) that the money was a personal gift from Tigran rather than a part of Mak'Ur salary.

A personal gift from Tigran? I do not know why this alarmed me, but I thought it was at best questionable ethics, and at worst...well...I did not know. Was it usual and normal over there? Or was it as odd in Armenia as it would be in the States? I had heard of executives forgoing their salaries or bonuses for the good of a company, but I had never heard of an exec giving a personal gift to his workers. Not to mention that Tigran had no formal role in Mak'Ur, so it would be more like some random man-on-the-street walked in and gave a bonus to some people. It concerned me, and I concluded that it was high time that I found out more about Tigran. So, I set up a dinner meeting with Valeriy.

He was one of the employees from the Yerevan office who was helping out our San Jose team at the time. Every now and then when it made sense we exchanged people between our two design centers. Mostly our San Jose design center 'borrowed' people from our Yerevan office. They had several good mathematicians there, and Valeriy was one of them, so when we delved into theoretical weeds, we borrowed their talent because it was cheaper and easier than hiring a local consultant.

Valeriy Voronoy was one of the two Armenians visiting us at the time. He was interesting, not only because he was a good applied-mathematician who had helped out before, nor because he was older than the average visitor from Armenia (I estimated in his early fifties), but also because he was half Armenian and half Russian. Apparently, according to some snippets of gossip that I'd picked up, something about his Russian or Ukrainian father, a famous professor of mathematics, who fell in love with his Armenian student, married her, and moved to Yerevan where he founded a faculty in the local university that, supposedly, ended up being one of the most highly respected centers of Pure Mathematics in Soviet times. The so called Voronoy Diagrams named after him are apparently still used in the best computational fluid dynamics tools for thermal and mechanical simulations. Or so I was told. Seemed like math ran in that family.

Anyway, I thought that Valeriy might be a suitable 'volunteer' to educate me about Armenia and Armenian ways. And since he was one of those talkative types who seemed to be always in the middle of various office corridor conversations, I hoped to pump him for information about Tigran. Perhaps a bit manipulative on my part but I needed someone to explain to me this 'personal gift' before I went off and embarrassed myself.

So I invited him to dinner at Original Joe's, an old-school Italian restaurant just a short walk from our office that was not only good but also served massive portions, something that I thought Valeriy might enjoy. Normally quite loud and full of energy, he struck me as the kind of a man who grabbed life with both hands and pretty much did everything to excess.

After we settled in, I asked him about life in Armenia and whether being only half-Armenian he had encountered any problems growing up there. He eyed me for a long time, as if pondering how to respond, and in the end said that this was something that he would not waste his time explaining to a regular American who would not have the foundation to follow any of it, but that I, as an ex-Yugoslav, might have a chance of understanding, and would therefore be worth the effort. He, like many of us Eastern Europeans, expressed himself both in speech and in writing, through long, convoluted run-on sentences that seemed to include all sorts of qualifiers and disclaimers baked in with the actual point that he was trying to make. After all my years in America where short and to the point communication was favored—often using only half sentences, I had forgotten about this tendency, and it took real concentration on my part to follow what he was saying. His accented English did not help either.

He explained to me that when he was growing up in Soviet Yerevan, the more pronounced divisions were along the country versus city folks, or maybe party apparatchiks versus regular people lines; and that since his father was perceived as a non-political academic who demonstrated his good sense by marrying an Armenian woman; and since his mother had a reputation that left no doubt that she would beat up anyone who might have picked on him, he had no problems. And that, in fact, even after the Soviet Union fell apart and independent Armenia was formed, the Armenians have had a warm relationship with mother-Russia, and were very welcoming to everybody and anybody as long as they were not Azerbaijanis. He added that many Armenians have moved to Russia since then and that many Russians stayed on in Armenia, too.

"But," he went on to elaborate, clearly enjoying the role of explaining things to an interested, even if perhaps somewhat naïve, audience, "if you knew how to read what was really going on below the covers, in those early days of independence, Armenian nationalism did bubble up to the surface, but very subtly so, and apparent mostly through the free-for-all privatization madness..."

He paused there, took a mouthful of his dinner, muttered something about decisions and which way to go, and then continued: "I will not bore you with stories from that time—it would take many dinners like this just to begin describing what happened, not just in Armenia but across the entire Soviet empire. I understand that you left Yugoslavia before its disintegration, but I am sure that your family and friends shared a lot of stories from that time, so you might be able to relate. Westerners—not a chance...

"It was total chaos," he continued. "The entire economy collapsed. National GDP dropped by half. There was massive unemployment and hyperinflation. It was bad in Russia, but worse in Armenia because we were much more dependent on them than they were on us. We were more or less knocked back into the pre-industrial era. And amazingly, throughout that crazy decade, amidst the chaos of a decomposing empire and a disappearing state, the powers in Yerevan—the real king makers—kept it together enough to make sure that the new class of capitalists who grabbed whatever was left in the wake of the Soviet collapse were Armenian, not Russian. Like...*strelets*... how you say in English? The Archer, for example..."

"The Archer?" I asked, somewhat confused, and purposely avoiding any talk about the chaos of the collapse of the Soviet empire. I have heard it all before. Tragic, but... Besides, talk about those times always made me feel somewhat guilty because I'd avoided it all, whereas my family and friends in Yugoslavia had suffered through it.

He laughed and almost instinctively looked over his shoulder, cleared his throat and said in an exaggerated whisper, "Your Tigran... Tigran Sakafian."

"*My* Tigran?" I questioned, surprised. Tigran's role in Mak'Ur was not supposed to be public knowledge, but I thought that denying it might turn Valeriy off. For all I knew, it may have been 'bazaar knowledge' in Armenia, so I ignored the implication and reacted with a joke. "We cannot possibly be talking about the same Tigran. The one I know is not only not *my* Tigran, but also happens to think that all of us are *his*... But why the archer?"

He laughed again, apologized in an exaggerated way, and explained that there was virtually an art form of coming up with good tags for famous people and popularly practiced by the café classes of Yerevan. He elaborated that this was carried over from the old Soviet days, when walls had ears and it was not necessarily wise to gossip about the *nomenklatura*, and that surely something similar must have taken place in Tito's Yugoslavia.

"But why the archer?" I repeated, ignoring the question about Yugoslavia. Nevertheless, back in my student days in Yugoslavia it had seemed like all the people in the news were tagged with some kind of a witty moniker. I'd never really thought about why. It was just funny.

"Ah, well," he explained, clearly amused, "Tigran actually means 'fighting with arrows' in old Armenian. Obviously, the Yerevan café intellectuals who came up with that clever tag were highly educated and knew archaic Armenian. And the name does suit *our* Tigran... There, is that better than *your* Tigran," he added, stressing the different possessives.

"Ah, I get it. But what did you mean about Armenian nationalism and privatizations?" I prodded.

This was getting really interesting, so I ordered another bottle of wine: a fine Gianfranco Fino, if I recall. At the time I was trying to learn my way around wines, and might have been using the occasion to try out a Primitivo from Italy. Another check mark on my list of Fat Cat credentials. But I took care to sip the wine sparingly, whereas Valeriy did not have such inhibitions. The wine seemed to have lubricated him quite nicely, and he was getting onto the topic that I wanted him to talk about.

"Well, in those early days, a combination of the government of the newly independent republic, plus the wealthy Armenians from abroad who cared about and invested in 'the cradle country,' made sure that privatized state assets went only to genuine Armenians. That is when and how the oligarchs were made, and they ensured that the few that we have were home-grown Armenians—none of the undesirable Russian oligarchs, or Kazakhstani or Persian money, or Turkish investors...

"The Archer was one of this anointed class," he went on. Valeriy seemed to be on autopilot now and I just let him talk. "His father was well connected—supposedly a wine merchant, like his own father, but only on paper. In reality that family was in the black market. Or so the rumors traded in the Yerevan cafes said. And to be successful in the black market one had to be very well connected to both sides..."

"Both sides?" I asked.

"Yes, yes, of course. Put yourself in the mindset of the Brezhnev era USSR. An operator in the black market had to be connected with the system, so that the police did not shut him down. And with the others in the underground, so that they did not kill him in order to take over his business." He explained patiently, eyed me critically to make sure I was following, and carried on. "So, our Archer inherited some good connections to both, the local police and the local mafia, plus he had the right nationalist credentials, and so his push to pick up some of the state assets was blessed, or at least not blocked, by the king-makers. In addition, he may have been lucky—or very wise, or a bit of both—and he picked up the right assets."

"Right assets?" I urged.

He sighed in a show of exasperation, clearly getting a bit bored with having to explain *everything* to me, and responded in the slow drone of a tired old lecturer. "The most desirable prizes at the time were the privatized Soviet built industrial concerns. But the majority of those actually went bankrupt shortly after independence..." After a sip of his wine, he added deliberately, "That always happens when the industry is built to achieve some political goal. Like the creation of the industrial

114

proletariat as proscribed by Marx, rather than because it made economic sense and it could make money…"

I presume he added that last editorial comment to make sure that even a slow listener like me understood.

"The oligarchs," he pressed on, "who fought over those sexy *industrial* assets—those that at the time looked like the premiere companies—did not pick wisely. They picked the wrong assets."

During a short interlude I asked the waiter about desserts, and Valeriy carried on. 'Singing for his dinner,' I thought to myself, quite satisfied with the setup.

"The Archer," Valeriy continued, "got into mining. At the time there was nothing sexy about it, but some of his mines are still in operation… Gold and maybe Molybdenum… He avoided the larger enterprises that dealt with commodity metals like copper or zinc. I guess he figured out that it would be hard to compete on an open global market against big mining in Africa and South America, and he let the bigger fish fight over those. They went out of business and he did not. Altogether, The Archer seemed to have a good nose for business and has a reputation of a competent oligarch who diversified into all sorts of different things. He is said to have built quite an empire: mining; wines and brandies; gold and diamonds; specialty furs and luxury goods; tobacco products… People say, maybe under the radar, drugs and perhaps even arms trade… But always high end. No one really knows…"

In a side conversation we agreed to forego the desserts, but I ordered another bottle of wine. Valeriy was on a roll and I wanted him to keep going. Wine in; story of Armenia and Tigran out.

"You know," he added in a slightly lowered voice, "back then, in those earlier days, all kinds of whispered stories about The Archer made the rounds. About 'inconvenient' people who had a mysterious tendency to disappear if they got in his way. Usually when he was branching out into some new line of business… Seems like these kinds of rumors have been absent lately. I wonder why."

This was now getting dangerously close to my worst fears. "So Tigran was like those oligarchs that are often in the news?

A bit of a thug with an army of private bodyguards who make sure that the boss is given proper respect?" I asked directly. "Like a *mafioso?*"

Valeriy burst out laughing, and it took him a bit to settle down again. "If everything isn't black and white, I say, why the hell not?" he responded in an exaggerated American accent. He then explained that this was his interpretation of a direct quote from John Wayne, that he was a fan of 'the duke,' and that the old western movies of his genre went a long way to explain America to foreigners who are puzzled by its apparent naiveté. He seemed very pleased with himself.

"Huh? You lost me."

He looked at me and said quite seriously, "C'mon, Professor. Put your Serbian hat on and stop thinking like an American. You see, while the cold war era Americans—as portrayed so well by John Wayne—sought to see everything as black or white, we—and especially the Soviet intelligentsia—spent all our energies arguing the finer points of the various shades of gray. We still do. All our literature is filled with stories that explore the paradoxes of life, that argue—mind you very eloquently so—the ambiguities of the many shades of gray, but that take forever to make a simple moral conclusion. It has always been that way—from Dostoevsky's *Crime and Punishment* to Bulgakov's *Master and Margarita.*" He laughed loudly, clearly feeling like he'd just made a very witty point, and remarked that this could well be the reason why America won the Cold War. "We like to describe our problems; Americans like to solve theirs," he concluded.

Maybe my wine was having too much of the desired effect. I did not follow what he was saying, and might have said so.

"There are stories like that about all the rich people in Armenia," he explained. "Disappearing enemies; inconvenient people meeting with mysterious accidents; all sorts of conspiracy theories... Clearly some of those stories say more about the wagging tongues of the Yerevan café clientele than about what actually happened. True or not, The Archer does have his fingers in many pies, and he might have had them bloodied every now and then. Who are we to judge if this was so, or if he was the victim or the aggressor, or if it was right or wrong? He certainly seems to have done whatever he has done, very well. It is not like he is a major billionaire; he is reputed to be 'modest,'" he added the air quotes for emphasis, paused to offer me some wine, and when I declined, he emptied the bottle into his glass, took a bit of a swig, nodded appreciatively, and carried on. "He has done okay and is probably just a *minor* billionaire. No one knows for sure." He smirked at his own cleverness.

I ordered another bottle.

"The Archer has avoided the pitfalls that other oligarchs fell into—either in business or in politics," Valeriy carried on without any prompts from me. "He seemed to know how to play his cards well and to stay on the right side of the system, unlike some of the others who consequently are not with us anymore. He played up his nationalist credentials and invested in his public image. Nothing crass like night club scenes with drugs and girls associated with other oligarchs. No, not our Archer; he was much more subtle. Every now and then a photograph of him at some public ceremony would appear— something like groundbreaking for a new church or school, or ribbon cutting for a sports stadium—and rumors that he'd funded the project would circulate. When he was seen at an art exhibition or a concert, newspaper articles implying that he was the sponsor would appear. Occasionally the local yellow press would claim that he was good friends with Charles Aznavour, which in Armenia is like saying that he was friends with God. Coincidentally, one of his wineries does have an 'Aznavour' label, reserved for the best reds. So, The Archer built up and cultivated this reputation of being a good Armenian, and a Good Samaritan. In a small country this kind of reputation is popular and celebrated. And given our large extended families, where everybody is connected through only two or three degrees of separation, popularity like that is a powerful form of protection. The politicians have learned to leave him alone…"

Another pause for wine; our third, or was it our fourth bottle?

"So, is that good or bad? Corrupt or philanthropic? Black or white?" he questioned, philosophically.

He was right. The atmosphere that he described reminded me of the stories about how things were in Yugoslavia during the wars. Local mafias and militias intertwined with corrupt politicians and nationalistic demagogues. Not quite relatable to my life and experiences in the US. Well, maybe, judging from movies and popular culture, things may have been similar here in the 1930s. A paternalistic Don Corleone or somebody, looking after his fellow immigrants... Who knows?

"Like that business of giving us bonuses as a personal gift," Valeriy went on. "That's quite typical of *our* Archer: a sure way to buy loyalty and to make us feel like he is *one of us* and to let us know that he looks out for us regular guys. The skeptics would say that he is just buying our silence—maybe even our complicity—in covering up something that does not bear the full light of day, if you see what I mean. I'm pretty sure that there is a shady side to our Archer, but to quote your president FDR: "He may be a son of a bitch, but he is *our* son of a bitch."

"Why?" I asked. "I don't get it. I thought you just said that he is simply a victim of gossip because he's rich."

"Well, maybe he is. Or maybe he isn't, and he just manufactured that image. But c'mon, Professor, think about it. The one common denominator of the Archer's business interests is high margin. All his known—and not so well known—enterprises are in the arenas characterized by high margins. That is a core tenet of his business philosophy which, incidentally, he is not shy about sharing. Newspaper articles, TV interviews, and the like all attest to this. Nothing bad there; nothing wrong with pursuing high margins. But," he said, raising his finger to amplify his point, "why would a man like that get involved with a software service business like CodeWriter? He was the owner, you know..."

"Tigran was the owner of CodeWriter?" I asked, surprised to say the least. This was even edgier than I'd feared. That put the 'personal gift' in a different light.

"Yes, yes, behind a veil or two as per his usual practice. I think that on paper he does not own anything at all—not directly. Well, maybe his clothes and a house in Yerevan are in his name. One of his shell companies was the listed owner of Code-Writer. You could say that he was just an investor diversifying into technology, and that it was not a lot of money for him. But why? Since when has software services been his kind of a high margin business? Never! So his interest in CodeWriter had to be motivated by other considerations. Some might say—not me; I am just a dumb mathematician who knows nothing—that this was most likely money laundering. Software services could make sense as a laundry. You pay the coders in Armenian Drams—possibly Armenian Drams that are not too clean—and you get paid for their services in US dollars or Euros or whatever. Even a low margin business like software services might be an attractive venture when it is combined with laundering money. I understand that the going rate for washing money can be as much as thirty percent. That would not be a big deal if you are in the drug business or something like that, where, I gather, the profit margins are on the order of one thousand percent. So a break-even software services company combined with a money laundry would in effect have a thirty percent margin. Not bad. And you ship the software across borders by simply pressing a button. No pesky customs officials to bribe, inventory books are easily cooked, track records to show to nosy government accountants are easily manufactured... Altogether, a great business if you are washing money..."

He stopped there and explained that all this was just speculation, that no one really knew, that these was just stories traded by the unemployed and idle in the Yerevan cafes. But by then his disclaimers sounded hollow at best.

"And when he sold CodeWriter to Mak'Ur—and I am not saying that Mak'Ur is complicit or dirty in any way—he must have realized some other gains. And in his typical and very wise ways, he is sharing some of the proceeds with the people around him. Two months' salary bonus for fifty Armenian engineers: not a big deal if along the way he washed a few million. And who is going to complain? Not me, for sure!"

He must have registered my befuddled expression because he looked at me with pity in his eyes. He mumbled something about me having been in America too long and that I must have absorbed the simplistic naiveté, but that being an ostrich may not be so bad, and that he was sorry to have robbed me of my fairy tales, and so on. He'd stopped making sense, and it was late.

He was slurring a bit, too. The last thing that he said, his accent a bit thicker than at the start of the evening, was an admonition.

"Professor, my friend, everything I just told you is nothing but rumor. I am just a mathematician and certainly do not know any more than the next wag in any café in Yerevan. Forget everything I said. The only part that I would believe is that you, my friend, should be careful when dealing with The Archer. He is not the kind of a man that should be taken lightly."

That stayed with me… I did not order another bottle.

A RATIONALIZATION

I brooded over that dinner with Valeriy for quite a while, fretting about everything that was said openly as well as what might have been implied between the lines. I turned it over in my mind not just the morning-after but for a few days; mornings over breakfast, evenings over a glass of wine, and many times in between. Partially to assure myself that what I remembered was not some alcohol-induced figment of my imagination and partially to sort out things that had actually been said from things that I might have invented, but mostly because I was a bit paralyzed and did not know what to do.

As far as I could tell, it was all real. Yes, Valeriy had said all those things, regardless how it did or did not make me feel; and no, I did not know what to do, knowing what I now knew. Or what I thought I knew... And it seemed to me that what Valeriy had said—café rumors or not—fit very well with everything else that I'd heard or knew about Tigran. I was now truly afraid. Because, if true, then we—Aram and I and our Mak'Ur AI Inc.—were most likely involved in something nefarious and possibly illegal. Even if we did nothing directly or knowingly, it was bad business.

Images of large men with stern faces wearing jackets emblazoned with 'FBI' knocking on my door in the middle of a night flashed through my mind, with bewildered Bev wrapped in a bathrobe staring on as they took apart our home and carted away all our computers and papers. Just like in the movies.

But assuming that it was as I feared and that we were complicit—or at least dirty—then what? How could we extricate ourselves from the mess? What was it that Tigran said when we'd first met? Something about no one walking away since that would be dishonorable and not much better than lying... And something about him being quite vindictive with people who disappoint him and betrayed his trust... Those remarks took on an entirely new meaning now, not sounding like the mere, albeit odd, platitudes that I'd taken them for at the time.

Images of my dead body being pulled out from a car wreck with some wayward mysterious black Audi—like in the stories of mafia executions that my Serbian and Montenegrin family talked about—flashed through my mind.

So simply walking away, or possibly even confronting Tigran, did not seem to be viable or wise options. Even going to the authorities, like those stern-faced FBI guys in my nightmare, did not seem smart since it was quite possible that nothing could be proved, or that proving anything might take years, which was plenty of time for Tigran to vent his 'disappointment,' again bringing to mind those so-called car accidents with mysterious black Audis.

On the other hand, if not true—if Tigran really was just a simple businessman maligned by envious and overly imaginative café gossips—then what? Then doing anything would not only be wrong but would also likely offend our Angel and possibly destroy our company. What to do?

One thing was certain. I needed to discuss this with Aram, face to face. Just the two of us. So I adjusted my travel schedule to intersect Aram's next coming to the States, which by that time was only once a month or so.

I told him everything—things that I knew plus the things that I suspected—expecting him to be shocked and outraged, but his reaction surprised me. Instead of being alarmed he was calm—entirely unperturbed. He simply nodded knowingly.

"Professor, I have heard similar things in Armenia. And more. Let me tell you, once those guys get used to you and adopt you—or at least stop treating you like some kind of an extraterrestrial—they invite you to spend time in the cafes and restaurants, and in their homes and churches, and... In that sense, Tigran was right and me being originally Armenian and speaking the language definitely helped. So they ask—more like

insist—on socializing. They introduce you to all kinds of people, who exchange all sorts of stories... And you hear things..."

"So?" I demanded.

"So nothing. I've heard it all before. And I have thought
about it a lot. Three things I got to suggest to you."

We were going for a walk in Riverside Park. Perhaps I was
getting overly paranoid, but I felt more comfortable talking
about this outdoors than in our office. I did not want Stiglitz to
overhear us, since I had my doubts about his level of complicity.
Or maybe I had seen too many Hollywood movies. And it was
a nice day.

"Number one," he started, holding up a finger, "everything
that you and I have heard is rumor. We do not really know
anything for a fact. And if back there they are anything like the
Armenian chatty yentas who fuel the gossip mill here, then I
would say that at least half of it is manufactured." He paused,
and before I could roll out all circumstantial evidence, he raised
a second finger and carried on.

"Number two; let us assume that it is true and that he is
laundering money through Mak'Ur. What is the big deal? Maybe I have spent too much time in Armenia, but the universal
belief over there seems to be that money laundering is a vic-
timless crime. In fact, they mostly think it is a smart thing to
do. Good business. You see, as they explained it to me, one of
the remnants of the socialist system that many of them grew up
in is that when everything belongs to the state, then nothing
belongs to anyone, and cheating the system is not just okay but
is in fact an honorable pursuit. Beating the system and stealing
something from the state—especially from a state that was perceived as somewhat distant and foreign—was something to be
proud of. They look at money laundering in that light, as if it is
beating an unfair system. And frankly, not only do I understand
it, but I am not sure that I disagree with them. Maybe not that
different from how many of our fellow Americans feel about
finding a new write-off or some loophole in the tax system..."

He paused there. I did not have a ready response. Truth be
said, it sounded a lot like the sentiments that my Yugoslav friends
and family often voiced. Still, that did not make it right...

"So," he continued, "let's say that Tigran *is* laundering money through Mak'Ur. Did you know that the IMF estimates that money laundering accounts for somewhere around three to five percent of the world GDP? It is true. I looked it up. That is around four *trillion* dollars a year. Whatever Tigran may or may not be washing is literally a drop in the ocean. It is not like stopping Tigran is going to change anything. Or even like it is going to put an end to whatever his other businesses that are generating the dirty dollars are doing, which ultimately may be something also fairly harmless like smuggling or operating on a cash basis to avoid taxes. So, what's the big deal?"

"Aram, it is illegal! People go to jail for money laundering," I protested. At least that part seemed to be black and white. "Forget the moral ambiguities and tradeoffs; it is illegal."

"And three," he continued ignoring my outburst and holding up three fingers, "let us say that we do decide to do something. What would we do? Report Tigran to Interpol or the FBI? Then what? Let us even put aside what Tigran may or may not do to us, there is no doubt that we would be stabbing him in the back. Would that be the right thing to do? He *has* helped us, and frankly, without him we would not be here. We report him and Mak'Ur would most likely end up being shut down. By now that would not be only you and me being out of a job, it would be more than one hundred families. Would that be the right thing to do?"

By this time I had calmed down a bit and realized that Aram was hitting on the same points that were lurking in the back of my mind. He was articulating them better than I had and seemed to have thought through the possible scenarios more thoroughly.

I responded honestly and maybe feeling somewhat defeated, "I do know that it is illegal. And I do know that I, personally, am not comfortable participating in anything like money laundering. But I do not know what exactly we should do."

We got to the Point, admired the view of the confluence of three rivers, and then started to walk back. A scattering of tourists were enjoying the park; mothers walking with babies, old people sitting on the park benches... Everything looked ordinary and serene. I felt a bit empty. I was all amped up and anxious to expose Tigran's crimes to Aram, and now that it was all out in the open between the two of us, it was as anticlimactic as post-coital blues.

"Well, professor, this is what I think: Let's stay the course. Let's do what we set out to do. Let's carry on building our company. Let's do all the things that we planned to do when we started…"

I did not know what to say, and he pressed on.

"Let's go for Round-B funding next, and grow big enough to be able to free ourselves of Tigran. Buy him out or dilute his share to the point where he and his money do not matter anymore. Let's cleanse Mak'Ur, so that someday we can say that it is what we wanted it to be—truly clean—and put all this unpleasantness, true or not, behind us."

Aram was back in his visionary mode, always driving forward. He clearly felt that we should co-opt Tigran and everything that was, or might be, shady by simply being successful, and not by confronting the issue or walking away from it.

"This is the best—and in my opinion, the only—concrete thing that we can do," he insisted forcefully. "C'mon, Professor, let's focus on raising that Series-B round and forget about rumors and innuendos. I believe that to be the greater good…"

I thought—realized—that this was just a bit too convenient a position for Aram to take. He was someone who for the last few years had had a one-track mind, entirely and solely focused on building the company. He had now tweaked his story to account for Tigran's possible illegal activities, but the outcome was the same as always: we press on and build Mak'Ur.

"Slippery slope," I thought. "In the end, this was justifying an illegal act for the sake of convenience," I thought.

"Aram," I said, "when you sleep with dogs you have to expect to wake up with fleas." I knew that this was an aimless platitude and not a strong argument…

So I let it go… Maybe the success of our company would be the best proof of our intent as well as the best revenge.

ROUND-B

Maybe I was jaded by that time. When we'd done Round-A funding, I was giddy and excited—breathless as a teenager on a first date. I lived and died in each meeting, my stomach in knots over the choice of each word I said. Now, here we were, eighteen months later and going for our Round-B funding, and I was almost blasé about it. During Round-A funding we had raised fifty-six million dollars and I thought that was a huge amount of money. But by now, considering the people we had hired, office and travel expenses, buying CodeWriter, the costs of designing and building the prototype product, and so on, we had gone through it quite successfully. Now we needed to raise three times our Round-A amount—$150 million—and I was all cool as a cucumber.

Maybe it was because by then I had spent enough time in the Bay Area, rubbing shoulders—well more like sharing drinks and meals—with 'the money.'Venture capitalists, investors, bankers, generic moneymen: to me they were no longer the priests of dark arts who had all sorts of mysterious powers and insights; they were just businessmen looking to make a killing. Some were nice guys; some not so much. I guess I got to know them pretty well and I knew how they thought, and consequently there was less suspense. I made the rounds ahead of time, prepped all the key people, listened to input, and knew what to say to whom and how to say it… And presto! We received commitments totaling $150 million.

Truth be told, it was not all down to networking and my glad-handing skills. No, our business was doing very well indeed, and the investors ponied up the money because they knew they were getting a piece of something good.

As planned, we entered the market with our smart-home software. And as predicted, the appliance makers led by Elvira, god bless her voluptuous heart, were open to collaborating with us. They knew that the AI-wave was coming and were mostly frightened by what the change might mean to them and their business. No one really knew for sure, other than that it was coming and that it would be big. So when we showed up with our ready-made software, with a ready-made integration plan for them to follow, they were happy to partner with us. This was partially because when it came to AI—something that they knew nothing about—we sounded like we were the experts who knew everything, and partially because our offering came to market at the right time and at a right price. But it was mostly because our software was a great handle for their hype, which they used as an excuse to raise their prices. It was easy for them to eat. That tag: "Compatible with IEEE STD 6769/ JEDEC JC-36 std 28B Smart Home Standard" was worth its weight in gold to them. In reality I am pretty sure that the tag, with its confusing alphabet soup, was totally meaningless gobbledygook to them and to any normal end-consumer. And yet it was worth the extra money that the appliance vendors charged simply because 'it was the future!' So, yes, we got quite a good uptake in the market, both for our interface standards and for our software.

The uptake was led by companies like Elvira's security system company that specialized in systems integration for high-end new homes. Also energy management companies who so cleverly bundled all sorts of things with solar panels so that their uptake was expected to shoot through the roof with climate change concerns. And the entertainment systems companies that integrated the various PCs, TVs, game consoles, and phones that people have in their homes with the power and convenience of AI. Furthermore, the expectations for the technology trickle-down into the mainstream new home market, and even into the retrofit market for existing homes, were all very promising.

And with that kind of adoption rate at the high end, all the appliances on the drawing boards also had to be compatible with interfacing standards and software management requirements. This started with the major big boxes—fridges and air conditioners and the like—but there was also talk of the trend trickling down to minor boxes like toasters and microwaves. Now who might want AI for their toaster was beyond me, but some makers seemed to think that it would be a good selling point.

So the uptake for our smart home software backbone was looking like it would go to plan, or even better than planned.

And yes, the little end user app also looked like it would have very good uptake, and the consumers seemed primed and ready to pay the extra few dollars for the privilege of being able to play with their smart-home data. I believed that Aram was right, and that the main selling point was probably the show-off factor. That too was expected to trickle down from trendy early adopters into the mainstream, and the expectation was for a stickiness of about eighty to ninety percent. That is, it was expected that at least eighty percent of the consumers buying new appliances would cough up the money for the app, and that would work out to more than one hundred million downloads in a couple of years!

And our hardware—our juggernaut—seemed set to follow a similar trajectory. The prototypes had been built and tested, and the clients were ready to spend some real money. We just needed to ramp up our product manufacturing, which was of course why we needed the Round-B funding.

But the thing that seemed to have excited the investors was our growing user data base, and the possibility of some potential ad revenue—or potentially some kind of market consulting services. After all, people's habits—how they behaved in their homes—would arguably be a source of different insights about them and their spending patterns than their Google searches or Facebook friendships. And we were the company who had access to that kind of data. It was ironic since our user database was originally intended to be just an undefined potential addition to our revenue stream, as we wanted it primarily to build better AI applications. Deriving revenue from it was meant to be padding, an 'also-ran.' And yet, for some of our investors this turned out to be our main attraction. It seemed like those investors were keen on getting in on at least a slice of the Google/Facebook advertising pie. I guess these days nobody gets fired for investing in companies that could someday become a Google or a Facebook.

The fact that a brilliant, inspired, genius reporter decided to write a piece on us—entirely unsolicited but very fortunate—did not hurt either. The article was published in the Technology section of the *New York Times* and was then picked up by all the internet news aggregators, and, all of a sudden, we were famous and had public name recognition—a footprint beyond just the AI circles or the tech community. He dubbed us 'The Practical Rube Company,' which I suppose was a witty way of grabbing eyeballs, but it seemed to work. He opened his article with voicing the common perception that smart appliances for the smart home of the future were simply modern Rube Goldberg machines, complicated devices and systems that do pretty much nothing of practical value. And he recognized the skeptics who believed that these devices would be just another gimmick pushed down the throats of unsuspecting consumers, that it was a waste of time and money at best, and the facilitator of the Big-Brother state at worst.

But then he reminded readers that most people reacted similarly to all new gizmos, and used the car as an example. From motorized windows to automatic headlights and windshield wipers, to the more advanced safety features of today and autonomous vehicles of tomorrow. And then he went on to elaborate how much safer, better and more comfortable the modern car was relative to its predecessors without the gizmos that were invariably dubbed—every time—as the 'unnecessary rubes.' And then he explained a few of the advanced features of smart homes that Mak'Ur was enabling and argued that they would be just as ubiquitous, convenient, and valuable as the automatic window wiper controls, and that our grandchildren would be just as unfamiliar with an unconnected home as our children are with a crank for opening car windows.

So purely by luck, we ended up with a good public image that came at just the right time. The article made excellent collateral for our hand out to the investors, and Aram had already started talking about using that 'practical rube' as a hook in advertising. Mak'Ur is Your Practical Rube... Good play on words— rube as in a naïve non-techie Mr. Anybody, and Rube as in Rube Goldberg machine.

Even though we were not yet profitable, our numbers looked very good, the potential for the future earnings seemed extremely promising, and we had a cool image. A trendy startup, we did not have a hard time getting the $150 million Round-B fully subscribed.

No doubt, our valuation was also buoyed by the irrational exuberance in the tech sector, which was to say that our timing was good. This was not so much luck as a matter of Luigi advising us on timing as well as the rest of the process. He helped to persuade one of the big VC firms into leading the round, since he felt it was too big for his boutique firm. After that, attracting the rest of the investors, as well as big institutional dollars was almost automatic. Who would not want to go in with a VC elevated to an infallible saintly status such as Andreessen Horowitz? We welcomed several new members to our Board of Directors.

So, I was a millionaire...at least on paper. Many times over, in fact. Amazing! Me—moi—a kid from the streets of Belgrade—a millionaire! It now seemed like leaving the University had been a wise decision after all, and that the Mak'Ur venture was a great success.

I had no interest in breeding specialized chickens, or even indulging in more mundane pursuits like acquiring a yacht and sailing around the world, or racing motocross, or skydiving. But one thing I considered as a way of spending some of that paper money was buying a condo in San Jose. Indeed, 'The 88' building on San Fernando Street looked very desirable—a short walk from the office, very nice condo units, spectacular urban views, good facilities with a gym and a pool and all sorts of services, a prestigious location... Why not? I was spending so much time in the Bay area that having my own place would be nice. And I might as well formalize my Fat Cat bi-coastal lifestyle. It would not cost that much, really. Maybe a bit north of a million. And maybe a car to go with it so that I didn't have to rent when I

came to the West Coast. That Aston Martin Vantage Roadster…
Now *there* was something worth drooling over!

I had not brought it up and talked it over with Bev yet, but
I was planning to do so soon. She, sensible as always, would
probably scoff at the idea, call it my midlife crisis, and otherwise
sneer at it—so I would need to slowly work her into the notion
when the time was right.

In truth, with all the flurry of activity associated with the
Round-B, I did not think that much about Tigran and the
source of his money. Maybe that was just a convenient excuse—since not thinking about it was far more comfortable
than brooding on the possible ugly truth. And those stern and
scary FBI men never came, and I had not noticed any black
Audis following me…

The round did accomplish something of what Aram suggested, since it diluted Tigran's holding in Mak'Ur down to around
fifteen percent—in terms of dollars, not votes. So—perhaps just
to placate my conscience—I could argue to myself that we were
moving in the right direction. What was it that Aram had said?
We were 'cleansing' Mak'Ur.

2020:
THE EXIT

STRIKE ONE

And then the Pandemic hit. The Coronavirus or the COVID-19 or the SARS-CoV-2 or whatever-the-hell-it-was-called. What the fuck!

I guess it was one of those times in history when the use of that phrase to convey the appropriate amount of surprise, and maybe some indignation, was not only permissible but fully merited. Perhaps comparable to what I presume was America's reaction to the Pearl Harbor bombing... Or that of the Romans faced by Hannibal's elephants coming from the north... What the fuck!?!

Epidemics were something that happened in other parts of the world, and occasionally affected a few unlucky Americans who had the misfortune to travel to the wrong place at the wrong time. Ebola, Zika, MARS, H1N1, SARS... whatever. But not here... Which goes to show what I knew.

The epidemic came closer as it spread throughout Italy—a place near and dear to me as it is close to home. Not at all as remote and distant as the jungles of Central African Republic and Brazil, or as exotic and potentially unhygienic as souks in the Middle East and wet markets in China...

But then it came here, fast, furious and dangerous.

We were all in the same boat—equally surprised, frightened and uncertain. And we, like the rest of the world, learned to cope. We worked from home, washed our hands, sheltered in place, practiced social distancing, wore masks, and followed all the other suggestions that the CDC made. Eventually we got used to it.

Although, some things one really did not want to get used

to. All the people dying, and the moving stories of families prevented from saying goodbye to their loved ones due to the isolation rules. Really sad. Heartbreaking. The cold-hearted objective view that held that this was a good pandemic since it was killing the old and the frail, and that it would be so much worse if it were killing the young and the healthy was mostly true, but not helpful. The optimists' historical view that claimed that all things being equal, humanity should lose around 250 million souls to match the toll of the last pandemic—the one between 1918 and 1920—also not helpful, other than rendering renewed respect for our grandparents' generation who lived through that right after surviving the horrors of WW1.

I confess that there was a part of the lockdown that I actually enjoyed. Staying at home for a while was nice. From a purely personal point of view—business class notwithstanding—I did not miss boarding a plane even a little bit.

And re-bonding with Bev was excellent—especially once we figured out a routine that gave both of us time and space to do our work and balanced out the home chores. Or maybe we just needed time to get used to each other again...

I didn't realize it, but I'd missed the comfort of the simple and the mundane, like watching TV together or deciding what to eat for dinner. I liked the warmth and security of waking up in my own bed with Bev right beside me. I liked our walks in the neighborhood, socially distanced or not. I'd missed Bev, and it was really good to be sharing the lockdown with her as we settled quite nicely into the new routine.

Having Lara at home from college was also great—a bit of a throwback to the days when she was living at home. Even better, since Lara had matured and not only deigned to spend time with us, but was also a pleasure to be around.

Those were the good parts, the proverbial silver lining.

But as they say, every silver lining has a cloud, and aside from all the restrictions to personal freedoms and lifestyle options, the bad part was the general coping with the new normal while trying to stay on the aggressive corporate growth curve. We had to execute to plan if we were to capture the rapidly growing market, although the response of the market to the pandemic was at that time anyone's guess. Still, markets wait for no one, and we had to be ready or someone else would be.

In fact, with the headquarters and two design centers located in three places separated by twelve time zones, we at Mak'Ur AI were already somewhat accustomed to phone and video calls at odd hours, so I guess we had a bit of a jump on the so-called new normal. We were used to relying on technology for communication, remote teams, and the like. Almost...

On the hardware side of the business—my turf—the key challenge was to rebalance our supply chain. We really had to scramble. We were just ramping up the production when the pandemic came with its lockdowns and disruptions to normal business flows. Our supply was in turmoil, to put it mildly. The multi-chip module architecture that we used made us especially prone to disruptions because we needed a balanced supply of a relatively large number of different sub-components. Any one small bit missing meant that the entire module would be no good. Even something mundane and stupid like lack of the right glue or right glass slides could shut us down.

On the other hand our principal suppliers—the foundry and the assembly house—were in Taiwan, so we were less impacted than many others because Taiwan had managed to control the outbreak of the disease without shutting everything down.

But it was not as if we went entirely unscathed. About a quarter of the items in our Bill of Materials were sourced from China, some of the chiplets along with the packaging substrates came from Korea, some from Japan, some from the US; many of the chemicals and assembly jigs were made in Germany, some in Austria, and our inventory storage and final test were in Singapore. Each one of those countries reacted differently at different times during the pandemic, so that managing the logistics was a hair-raising touch-and-go ride for a while. There were quite a lot of disruptions.

Much like everybody else in the industry, we coped as best we could. In fact, we were luckier than some in that we were just ramping up rather than being in full production, so we did not have to manage too many of those uncomfortable calls informing our clients that we could not meet our commitments.

Just Elvira, Inc. and a few others. The disruptions in our supply chain still mostly impacted the products on the clients' drawing boards, which made it easier for them to endure the delays.

We were not in a position to on-shore everything. That would have been too expensive even if we could find suitable American suppliers for all components, and even if those suppliers did have spare capacity. Similarly, we could not achieve full redundancy for every line item in our Bill of Materials—again too expensive and too complicated. But we did scramble to identify what we felt were the highest risk links in the supply chain and tried to build in some resilience by having second sources and/ or excess inventory for select items. In particular, after some heavy-duty negotiations, we managed to second-source some of the suppliers in China with compatible components from Japan; we over-ordered and tried to build a buffer inventory of chiplets and a few other critical components, we stood up back-up Assembly and Test capability in Taiwan, and replicated finished goods storage and shipment operations as well as the final test capability in America. It was expensive, but good.

By midsummer I felt like we were coping relatively well, and that all we had to do was to carry on and ride out the pandemic.

STRIKE TWO

Yield Bust! The two words that keep every semiconductor technologist awake at night. Strike two!

As per standard industry practice, we designed and verified our hardware architecture using prototype modules. We built those using engineering samples from our chiplet vendors, engineering wafers of our custom silicon produced by the foundry, and engineering packaging lots run by our Assembly and Test services provider. Everything looked good. We then built and/or bought a small volume of all the sub-components, assembled and tested a sample population of modules, and completed the usual qualification and reliability tests. All standard practice...

We were ramping up our volumes when the pandemic hit. And just as we were reestablishing our supply chain, a significant proportion of the product modules, which just happened to be the parts that we were building for Elvira, Inc., started to fail the final outgoing test. Not all modules failed, but enough of them did to be worrisome. We naturally rushed the backup material through the production pipeline hoping that the yield loss was a fluke. We even coughed up the exorbitant money required to upgrade our material to 'hot lot' status to accelerate the throughput. But it was no good. The high failure rate persisted, sporadically so, but still there was no way we could pretend that it was not real. We were in the middle of a Yield Bust!

Even as one who had spent his entire career in the academic ivory tower, I knew that such things happened. Every semiconductor engineer has told or heard horror stories about yield busts.

Basically, the nature of semiconductor technology is that the number of good parts that come out at the end of a production line is never equal to the number of units that are started at the beginning of that line. Statistical variability of the manufacturing processes, handling accidents and breakage, contaminants and defects, and all sorts of interactions and other horrible things can—and do —happen. This is normal. The ratio of the good parts that come out to the number of parts that have been started is called 'yield.' This number is always closely watched because it drives the profits. The fate of individual careers, products, and even whole companies often hang on that ratio. The semiconductor industry lives and dies by yield. But every now and then that proportion plummets—sometimes down to zero. That is a semiconductor engineer's nightmare known as a 'yield bust.'

Frankly, knowing what I know—knowing how tiny and finicky the electronic devices really are, how many billions of them there are on every single chip, how even an atom or two out of place can cause a failure, how many bizarre interactions there can be—I am amazed that any of the ICs ever do work. But they do. Miraculously so. Most of the time...

For the kinds of ICs and modules that we were building, yields of the order of eighty to ninety percent should have been the norm. The yields that we were actually seeing for various production batches varied between four percent and eighty-six percent. Averaged to about thirty percent. Inconsistent and unpredictable. Yes, we were in the middle of a goddamned yield bust.

When a yield bust happens it is the proverbial code red. Everybody scrambles and goes into a fire-fighting mode: drop everything other than activities that directly impact the yield problem and work 24-7. All sorts of tiger teams are formed, all kinds of analyses are done, the bug that caused the failures is hopefully found, a suitable fix is defined and implemented, new material is started in the production line, and then the world gets back to normal. The trick is to get to that point rapidly and to fix the problem without having to scrap a lot of inventory. And to do it without pissing off a bunch of customers and losing too many design-in slots to competitors. The history of the industry is littered with the carcasses of companies that went out of business due to a yield bust that they could not fix in time. In a way—perhaps aptly put in this day and age—a yield bust is like a pandemic for chips.

Debugging a failed integrated circuit required to identify the root cause of the yield bust is a mind-boggling dark art at the best of the times. It calls for many very specialized tests, tools and skills, a lot of collaboration between multiple different engineering specialties and organizational teams, disciplined analyses, patient elimination of possible causes of failures through logical deduction until the culprit is identified. And oodles and oodles of luck. Saying that it is looking for a needle in a haystack is an understatement. Literally—since the objective often is to find that one transistor out of the ten billion that are integrated on a modern chip that is not working the way it was supposed to.

But doing all that during a pandemic? Scrambling up the right tiger teams, organizing and rushing through all kinds of new lot starts, coordinating the different tests and analyses, brainstorming failure models and validating all kinds of theories, with turnaround times that only a downed production line could justify, all while everybody is supposed to be safely sheltering at home? Good luck!

Analysis of standard production data was something that even a team in a lockdown could handle well enough: our industry is probably better than most in terms of keeping all sorts of production data in various databases in various clouds, which could be accessed remotely from anywhere. So we could address the obvious questions fairly quickly. For example, were the failures correlated in any way to the changes in our supply chain precipitated by the pandemic? Or were the failures correlated to any parametric excursions, manufacturing lots, time frames, equipment maintenance rotation, or even specific operators working the line, and so on? Unfortunately no, no, no and no. Those would have been relatively easy things to fix. It seemed that we were not that lucky.

Even exploring the various 'what-if' scenarios to see if a specific failure mechanism could be reverse engineered to replicate the observed failure modes through different modeling and simulation exercises—something that we engineers love doing—was reasonably compatible with lockdowns. But, unfortunately, we could not identify a definitive culprit mechanism that would explain all our observations.

Short of those easy scenarios, resolving the bug that precipitated our yield bust necessarily called for proactive tests and analyses with real parts—not just retroactive looking at the existing data. Failed units had to be analyzed. This involved physical deconstruction and all kinds of specialized physical inspection procedures, oftentimes known to no more than a dozen people on the planet armed with some very esoteric tools and capabilities. New material had to be built, with very specific skews in the manufacturing processes, and subjected to new test conditions and/or physical evaluations. This called for moving parts and making sure that the right people, with the right skills, armed with the right tools and capabilities, converged with the right parts at the right times.

Even under normal circumstances coordinating all that would be challenging, but it was nigh impossible to do while the entire world was locked down due to the pandemic. And trying to do any of it promptly, with a turnaround time that matched the panic level sense of urgency where 'by yesterday' was too slow and too late was totally impossible.

Meanwhile, the need to solve the problem and the cost of a downed production line ratcheted up with every passing day, pandemic or not.

This was maximum pressure, and everybody in Mak'Ur and beyond who could possibly contribute anything to the effort was recruited. I felt like the problem was ultimately on my shoulders and between the frantic calls to our teams in San Jose and Yerevan, to our suppliers in Taiwan, Japan, Korea and Shanghai, to various specialty labs and prima donna consultants whose help we needed, and the worrying and fretting that kept me up nights, I felt like I had not slept in weeks.

Given the apparent complexity of the problem, the length of a cycle of learning for our modules, and the production turnaround time, I estimated that if we were lucky, we could solve the problem in maybe three months, but it would probably take five or six months.

The impact on overall corporate operations had to be

minimized. It was absolutely critical that we ramp up production, hold on to the design slots, and get some revenue—even token revenue—from hardware sales. We could blame the pandemic for some delays, but the market was moving, and if we missed the train, so to speak, we could lose the window of opportunity and end up out of business. So we had no choice; we had to go into 'stupid-mode' and throw money at the problem by increasing the production rate so that even with reduced and inconsistent yields we could get out enough good modules to keep going.

That was hoping that whatever was the mechanism responsible for the yield bust would not also cause some kind of a reliability issue which could precipitate further failures downstream. Maybe failures in the appliances with our modules in them. Or—nightmare scenario—fires in people's homes caused by our modules. If a scenario like that played out, we would be not only out of business, but possibly also liable for damages or injuries. Like Takata with their air-bag inflator.

But there was no indication of that kind of failure mechanism in our case, so after much debate and soul searching, we decided that the risks were purely financial and that ramping up the production to cover the yield loss would just be throwing good money after bad. It meant that we would not only be not making profit, but would in effect also be stapling perfectly good money to every part that we shipped. In fact, most of the time we would be building crap that we knew we would throw out. The company would be hemorrhaging cash, and it was a really stupid way to operate, but it was either that or closing the doors right away.

The fate of Mak'Ur AI hung in balance. Either we solved the yield problem before we ran out of money, or we went out of business immediately. There were no other options. We prayed for a miracle.

STRIKE THREE

Tigran called on my home landline and said that he needed an urgent partners meeting, and that he was organizing a flight for us to Cyprus, and to be ready to stay a few days.

I was surprised by the call, to say the least, and barely managed to voice my concerns about the wisdom, or for that matter the sheer feasibility of international travel at a time like this, meaning both during the pandemic and in the middle of a yield bust. But he replied in a terse and somewhat testy tone that he was scrambling up a private jet for our flight, that we would be meeting in his private villa close to Paphos, that there would be a private car to drive us to and from the airport, that his staff is routinely tested for COVID, that Cyprus has managed the spread of the virus quite well, and, in short, that I could trust him that he had made it safe for all. Then he abruptly ended the call.

I had no opportunity to question the purpose for the meeting, or its urgency. Within two minutes after the call had ended an e-mail including instructions with the details of the arrangements arrived. It was clear that this was not up for debate. It seemed more like an order than a request.

I had never heard of Paphos and had to look it up on Google Maps. South coast of Cyprus. Judging from the online pictures and write-ups it looked like an idyllic place, very scenic in a Mediterranean way with perfect weather and a history going back to the ancient Greeks. I guess all those Russian oligarchs who supposedly kept their excess money in Cyprus, and who often bought the local passport and relocated there, may not have been so dumb after all.

I called Aram and he had been equally surprised by Tigran

and did not have any insights about the purpose and the timing of the meeting. So we called Stiglitz: ditto.

Bev was not pleased. Truth be told, neither was I. But on further reflection I concluded that at least as far as coronavirus was concerned Tigran was probably right. Flying in a private jet and meeting in a private house—both presumably sanitized—was a reasonable thing to do. I tried hard to convince Bev of this, but without much success.

But, I did not feel that Tigran had left us any choice...

So on the designated date a van with 'Concierge MD' written across its side brought a couple of technicians, each looking very professional with their white lab jackets and stethoscopes, to administer a standard nose swab PCR test for COVID-19 right in my study at home! They threw in a gratuitous check of blood pressure, pulse, temperature, and all the other usual preliminaries.

And presumably I tested negative, as a few hours later a limo came to collect me, made a stop to get Aram and Stiglitz, and after a half hour ride deposited us at the General Aviation Terminal of the airport. We were met there by a young lady sporting the uniform of Victor International who asked to borrow our passports and walked us directly to a gleaming jet, all the while gushing about the comforts and qualities of our Gulfstream G550. She assured us that it was one of the best of that type of airplane and that we would surely enjoy the ride. I wasn't really listening—mostly over the moon about skipping the TSA security line, the boarding pass check-in line, the passport check line, and other lines that mere mortals normally have to deal with.

On board we were met by the crew who assured us that they too had tested negative, that the plane had been deep-cleaned, and that there was no need for masks or social distancing. We were reunited with our passports, accompanied with a glass of champagne, of course. And then we were off!

Actually the ride itself was a little bit noisier and bumpier than in a normal transoceanic jetliner, but the amenities and services, not to mention the freedom to move around and the quality of the seat/bed, easily made up for it. Definitely worth every penny of Tigran's money. The food: a four course succession of delectable treats... The booze: aperitif, white, red, cognac, port... The flight attendant: more like 'a stewardess' with all the outdated associations that went with that title—a friendly exotic beauty from somewhere in southern Asia in a dress so snug that it was hard to understand how she managed to move... We slept in a proper bed, which was followed by an on-board shower. This was clearly, the *only way to travel*...

We spent a good portion of the flight speculating about the upcoming meeting. I was concerned that it was to talk about the yield bust, and felt a bit like I had been called to the principal's office to explain myself. But Stiglitz said that that was not what Tigran wanted to discuss. "Not his kind of a thing," he reassured me. On the other hand, he swore he had no further insight into Tigran's motives and/or intentions. Aram was mostly silent, probably brooding and worrying about his company. And probably just as disturbed by the 'how' versus the 'what' of this meeting as I was.

We landed at Paphos airport just before sunset and were greeted by the unmistakable aromas of a Mediterranean evening: cypress and citrus trees, oleanders, the smell of the sea. A uniformed man met us, took care of the usual bureaucratic procedures, and whisked us off in one of those giant SUVs with heavily tinted windows and a well-equipped bar. Everything occurred exactly according to the arrangements that Tigran had described in his e-mail, but so much more impressive in real life.

The place that Tigran had called his 'villa' turned out to be a walled-in, gated estate perched on a hilltop with a spectacular view of the coastline and the sea. The complex included a large garage, a tennis court, an extensive garden, and three buildings arranged in a horseshoe pattern around a central pool. The houses were of the modern geometric architectural style, not the traditional Mediterranean look that I was expecting: gleaming white, with a flat roof and faceted sides interrupted by giant tinted windows and all kinds of angular balconies tucked in here and there. We were taken to one of the buildings—presumably the guest pavilion—shown to our respective suites, and told that Tigran would join us for dinner on the pool veranda at 9:00 o'clock.

Plenty of time for a quick shower and a rest... Maybe even

a peek at e-mails to check on the status of various activities that were in process; and, of course, an opportunity to drop a line to Bev to assure her that all was well.

By 9:00 it was dark but still balmy, with a refreshing breeze wafting in from the sea. Tigran appeared seemingly from nowhere dressed in loose fitting white pants and a crêpe shirt. He waved us to the table as he politely inquired about the flight, the rooms, the welcome we'd received and other trivialities. When we'd settled around the table, our glasses were properly filled and various appetizers were spread in front of us, and after the mute staff disappeared, he did the double rap on the table with his ring and became serious.

"I know that you are wondering why I asked you here," he said in a pedantic and determined tone. "I know that I would be if I was in your place... As per the original agreement between us—the three equal partners in Mak'Ur—I need a fundamental rethink." His opening statement was followed by a suspenseful pause. "I believe that the company is growing very well. You gentlemen have done an outstanding job. Congratulations... So it is not at all that I think that the business is bad, or anything negative, but, unfortunately, for reasons that I do not want to go into, I must cash out. So we must discuss how to dissolve our partnership."

I was stunned. What could one say to an unexpected revelation like that? Strike three!

"Fortunately, we set up the company structure correctly," he went on, with a nod at Stiglitz, "and between us we own enough class-A shares to make whatever decisions are necessary. We clearly must agree on how to implement a change in the ownership in Mak'Ur., how to maximize the value of the company for each of us, and also how to minimize the impact on its operations and employees."

We, like Tigran's minions that we were, remained sullen and silent.

"I know that this is a surprise to you," he continued in the same level tones that he always used. He might as well have been talking about the weather. "And you have had a long day... So I propose that we dive into the details tomorrow. In fact, I have set aside the whole day to deal only with Mak'Ur business.

I want to give you time to digest the news and to set aside any denials or surprises or emotional responses. We are grown men and need to deal rationally with the situation."

His steady calm gaze scanned our faces—as if to make sure that we had received and understood the news as well as his instructions.

"Breakfast is at seven o'clock," he continued, rising from the table. "We start the day a bit early here so that we can accommodate a siesta during the heat of the day. See you then."

ENGINEERING AN EXIT

Next morning started out as an incongruous contrasting scene, somewhat reminiscent of those Hollywood movies where they show the happy protagonists frolicking in the sun before the plot develops and all kinds of horrors come out...

The setting was pristine and tranquil, birds chirping, clear pale blue sky, long shadows cast by the light of the sunrise, dusty green of olive trees, the calming sound of a trickling waterfall with an expansive view of the valley and the shoreline beyond the infinity edge pool. A mist hovered over the azure sea. A few boats floated peacefully on the calm water. Heavenly!

But the mood was somber and ominous, conveying a sense of loss and foreboding. No one seemed to want to talk because talk would be depressing.

The three of us gathered round a continental style smorgasbord breakfast set up on the veranda—croissants and all sorts of rolls, several types of sliced cheese, butter and cream cheese, cold cuts, salmon and herring, boiled eggs, jams, yoghurts, juices, fruits... All very delicious looking, but we were focused mostly on the coffee. We were more than a bit groggy due to lack of sleep.

I hadn't had a very good night as the effects of jetlag were compounded by the stress of the yield problem that I, of course, had to check up on. And Tigran's news was not conducive to my usual good sleep either. I suspected that the same was true for Aram and even for Stiglitz.

I guess what they say is true: When you start a company you end up with an emotional anchor. It is not rare for entrepreneurs to make their startups the center of their lives and to talk about them the way parents gush about their kids. I have seen it often at various socials in the Bay Area.

For me, personally, it was not supposed to be that extreme—perhaps because I was, after all, the 'resident adult,' and presumably somewhat more mature than an average tech entrepreneur. Nevertheless, I was not prepared to let Mak'Ur leave my life. Not yet. Not this way. Tigran's revelation was certainly disconcerting, like someone with whom you had partnered to bring up a child was asking for a divorce and you had to give up custody. Hurtful... Alarming... Frightening... I was already feeling a sense of loss, as there were still so many things that I wanted us to do.

Honestly, I had not thought about life after Mak'Ur, so maybe a part of my gloom was just anxiety about what might be next for me. A change—and to make it worse—an unplanned change. I was feeling unsettled and anxious, sad and scared.

Judging from his long face, Aram was probably feeling similarly. Even Stiglitz looked distraught—like he had developed an emotional bond with our enterprise.

Aram broke the silence, probably trying to shake off the sullen mood, "It's not all bad. The timing *is* a surprise. But the outcome is not. Exiting Mak'Ur is what we've been working for all this time. We knew that this was coming sooner or later. It's just a bit sooner than expected."

"True," I responded, picking up on the thread. "Maybe this is a bit like parenting. After all, you have kids, you love them and raise them and do all the things that parents do, only so that they will go away. The very last thing you want for them—or for yourself—is for them to stay at home with Mom and Dad."

"Exactly!" Tigran broke in as he joined us.

"We should talk about the *how*, but the *what* is all good. We shall all make money. That *was* the purpose of the enterprise, was it not? The question is how much we will make. But you gentlemen have done such a good job that there is very little doubt that we *will* make some money, and that you three shall be rich men."

Tigran did not seem morose. After we settled around a table, he made the statement that was to shape the rest of the day's discussions: "I need to get about 150 million out of Mak'Ur. US dollars, of course. Which means that we must get the company valued at about a billion. So Mak'Ur is a unicorn. Congratulations gentlemen and thank you… I mean it, thank you. You built a unicorn." He came as close to a smile as I have ever seen him come. "Given how much I have put in, this has been one of my best investments," he added.

"A billion?" Aram reacted, with a mixture of surprise and perhaps doubt. "It wasn't so long ago that we struggled to raise the 150 million in Round-B. Optimistically, we could get our annual revenue somewhere to that range in a year or so. And if we were to sell the company then, and if we managed to get a multiplier of, say four or five, then that could get the valuation up to 600 to 750 mils. But a billion? It would take us a while longer to get there." He was doing the math, and clearly was skeptical about a unicorn valuation.

"Well, 150 is what I need," Tigran repeated. "And, I need it in about three to five months. Not a year or two."

"A billion within three months? While we are in the middle of a yield bust and hemorrhaging cash? That is…very difficult," I said, stopping myself from saying something like 'fucking impossible' for fear of appearing closed and negative. But I did feel that some realism had to be injected into this conversation and that someone had to remind Tigran that we were in fact on the brink of disaster.

"Well, I do need to get out about 150 in about three months," Tigran responded, totally unphased. "And that is not negotiable. The reason we are here is to figure out *how* we can make that happen. Not *if*…"

As usual, he left very little room for ambiguity. So we spent the day discussing the various possible exit strategies…

We quickly agreed that the obvious solution was to have the existing investors buy out Tigran's share. But we concluded that this was unlikely to generate the kind of money that Tigran needed, especially not in the timeframe he needed it in. Even if we did assume that we could wave a magic wand and make the yield problem go away, and even though Tigran's shares were Class-A shares that came with weighted voting rights, at this stage it was still unlikely that we could talk any current investor into taking on more risk. In fact, Tigran, or for that matter any of the other seed investors, cashing out at this stage was, if anything, likely to make the rest want to exit too. Not to double down...

We explored the possibility of bringing in a new external investor—a VC or private equity or even some institutional guys—who would be willing to buy out Tigran's share. But it was not like our round B was oversubscribed. And that was before the pandemic and the yield problems. The pandemic— perhaps surprisingly so—in fact had a positive impact on the market, and the high-tech valuations were quite frothy. But a valuation of a billion—a sevenfold increase relative to our Round-B—so soon after it? Unlikely... And the yield issues and the associated cost run-rate would certainly depress any such interest.

Somewhere in there lunch was served. Something light— seafood and salad. No booze. It was a working lunch. I think by then we had started to realize that the only way to get to the kind of numbers that Tigran wanted would be to sell out the entire company rather than just his piece.

We discussed the possibility of doing an IPO. Of course, this was something that we had talked about—perhaps fantasized about—in the past. But realistically, we were not planning on it for a couple of years—not until the company was established and generating some real revenue. So going for an IPO now would have to be a balls-to-the-wall Hail-Mary effort. It did not take us long to agree that an IPO would be challenging, if not impossible, to manage within three months. Even if we did line up an underwriter overnight, and even if they pitched up the IPO in zero time, the lock-up period alone would be beyond Tigran's time horizon. And in reality, especially for a unicorn positioning, we would need the most prestigious un- derwriters, who would need several months to do their due diligence to set up the legal framework and to whip up the buzz in the market. Realistically six to nine months. At least. Plus the lock-up period.

We broke for siesta, but pleasurable as it was, it did not pro- duce any epiphanies. We met again for afternoon coffee served by one of the silent staffers offering ice cream and Greek cookies with the coffee. We carried on our deliberations...

We talked about trying to find some kind of a private equity hedge fund that would be willing to buy out the entire company—a perfectly respectable exit and not such an unusual situation. But we did not think that we could get anywhere near a billion with our current cash flow picture. Private equity hedge funds could be faster than an IPO and could pony up a billion, but only if they saw a cash flow that would give them a return on investment within a few years. Even then, it would most likely take them many months to make a decision...*if* they decided to proceed. After all, the smart-home market was just starting to develop, and with the world locked down in a pandemic no one knew which way things would go. In all likelihood they would probably run away from the risks, and from our current yield issues...

Tigran listened to our discussion, nodding here and there, but did not say much. The impression that I had was that he was simply allowing us to catch up and come to the conclusions that he had already reached. At around sunset Tigran seemed to wake up. His body language changed leaving little doubt that he had something to say. He did his double rap on the table with his ring, and we instinctively fell silent and looked at him, waiting. In his calm and steady way he proceeded to make it clear that he thought that this was an excellent discussion, and that we had explored all sorts of possibilities, but now it was time to stop admiring the problem and draw some conclusions.

"There are two imperatives," he stated, enunciating the word deliberately, somehow giving the impression that he had thought long and hard about the selection of a perfect word. "One: it is vital that the yield problem, and the associated cash flow issues, go away... We need Mak'Ur to look like it is either profitable *now*, or at least securely on its way to profitability..."

I am not certain of this, but I thought that he was looking at me when he said that. Maybe I was just imagining it, but I definitely felt that the onus for the yield issue was on me. "We need more time to make the yield problem go away," I protested, repeating his words. "If we are lucky—a few months just to debug the problem. And then another couple of months to reload the pipeline. Barring a miracle, it is just not possible to identify and fix a bug of this kind and ramp-up the production line in less than three months."

"You do *not* have three months," Tigran snapped, showing something of a temper for the first time. "If you cannot fix it, then make it *look* like it is fixed. The problem has to be off the table." Leaving very little doubt that this was not optional, he repeated, "It is imperative!"

"Tigran," I reacted, tamping down my fear but feeling defensive and a need to explain, "that is how long it takes. I can explain it if you want. It is complicated. As for making it *look* like it is not there," I played back his emphasis, "there is no such thing as a secret in our industry. We cannot just pretend that there is no problem. Our people know. They have friends in other companies. People in our supply chain know. They have friends. In our industry word gets around fast. No secrets." I tried to reason with him and make him understand the realities.

"Then *manufacture* a legend that it is fixed," he rapped the table with his damned ring again as he stared coldly at me. Just a stone-cold order. "It is imperative that you make it go away."

I was left with a feeling that the part that went unstated was that if I could not make it happen —if I refused to, or failed to make it go away—he would find someone who would. Was this an unstated threat? Perhaps I was imagining it.

Back in his level monotone, and turning to Aram and Stiglitz, Tigran continued, "We need to whip up an IPO-like frenzy and drum up market expectation of a valuation of one billion or more. And then we need to find a private equity firm that will take the company off the market..."

They were both smarter than I was and did not argue with Tigran. They did not protest that this could not be done or that it was an unreasonable expectation. In fact, Stiglitz spoke up saying that in an exuberant market enamored by the technology sector, there was some recent history of pre-IPO valuations that were driven up with the right kind of a buzz. Even before the pandemic. He mentioned Uber and WeWork as examples. He added that nowadays a one-billion-dollar valuation in the tech sector was really not that exorbitant.

Aram was uncharacteristically quiet but with a gleam in his eye. I think that branding Mak'Ur a unicorn company had somehow captured his imagination. He was inspired by the possibility. He *wanted* it to be so. And therefore, he was conspiring to make it so.

Like the previous night, dinner was served on the pool veranda. Aram and Stiglitz, goaded by Tigran, were engrossed in a discussion about ways to generate the pre-IPO frenzy and the methods of finding suitable underwriters. "We have to think big," Tigran emphasized. "With a straight face," he added, implying that he fully understood that the challenge was that of setting up the right kind of a front rather than of communicating the truth. And by the time the desserts were served, they had agreed between themselves that if we were to be successful, then we would need to whip up the frothiness for the entire smart-home sector, not just for Mak'Ur, and that we would have to milk the trend. "Yes, yes," Tigran agreed. "Think big!"

They then started to speculate about launching a SPAC or maybe an ETF as a possible way of working up the right kind of excitement in the market and accelerating the process of a sale. And I think it was Stiglitz who proposed that such a SPAC could then also be used as a way of facilitating anyone buying out Mak'Ur. "A preemptive move to reduce the barriers to acquisition," he said.

Aram suggested that perhaps a consulting contract with someone like Bain could also be used to drum up interest in the smart-home sector, and maybe even put Mak'Ur on the radar of Bain Capital—a private capital entity known to have poured billions into the tech sector.

They were in full-blown brainstorming mode, considering a veritable alphabet soup of tools and derivatives and funds that could be brought to bear. As they pumped themselves up, it reminded me of what I had seen good salespeople do before a meeting with a tough client. They engaged in mutual massaging of their egos to amp up their self-confidence, and convinced themselves that they could—and would—pull off a deal.

But I had stopped listening. I was far more worried about my 'assignment,' my part, and my skin.

With all the brilliance of hindsight, I had to admit that Tigran was either a natural manager or someone who had been coached by a real professional. He clearly allowed us time to spin our wheels and then come to conclusions that he already had drawn, but that we would have challenged had we not explored the various possibilities ourselves. And having led us there, he was now issuing orders and bolstering our attitudes. Like a coach in his locker room, he was past the point of discussing how the game would be won and was now pumping up team spirit and orchestrating the right morale.

Of which I had none... I did not think that the problem that Tigran parked at my door was solvable, and I was worried about the consequences. I was frightened. "What now, genius?" I yelled at myself. The rest of the evening was a blur to me; I was not registering any more.

NIGHTTIME VISITOR

It was around midnight and just before I went to bed—unexpected so I almost missed it—but, yes, definitely, there was a gentle knock on my door. I was shocked to find Tigran standing there wearing a friendly smile and carrying a bottle and two cognac glasses in his hands. "May I come in?" he asked, and I stepped aside to let him enter. "A nightcap," he suggested, raising a bottle of Ararat Dvin cognac.

We settled in the living room part of the suite—him in an armchair with his feet up on the ottoman, me reclining on the sofa. With snifters in hand, I am sure that it *looked* quite cozy. But it was not. I was tense.

"Professor," he began, "when we first met, I promised that I would always say what I thought. So, I will tell you exactly what is on my mind…" After a deep inhalation of the rich aroma of the cognac, then a small sip, he got into it.

"I am not worried about the unicorn valuation. I believe that Aram and Stiglitz will pull it off. At his core, your Aram is a salesman; maybe a crusader too. He is passionate about converting people to his point of view. From what I have seen of him, when there is a cause that captures his imagination, he is unstoppable. I suspect that what really drives him is the thrill of the sale, rather than the cause itself. There are people like that, don't you think?"

I shrugged noncommittally. I knew that he was probably right, but it had taken me longer to understand this about Aram.

"On the other hand, *my* Stiglitz," he carried on, stressing the 'my', "is a hard-core technocrat. It is the solving of a problem that motivates him. Like a machine… You know, I first interviewed him because of his MBA thesis—something about money laundering and prevention—and right from the beginning he advised me to keep all money of questionable origin in Europe, and to transfer it to the US only if it was totally untraceable..."

At that point I might have fidgeted a bit, since this topic made me uncomfortable, but Tigran just carried on unperturbed.

"The thing that really caught my attention was that this was not because of any legal or moral concerns that he might have had. (I do not think that he is encumbered by such baggage.) Rather his reaction was purely practical. There was a technical problem in front of him and his professional duty was to solve it. He explained that the American Fed and FBI were extremely strong, thanks to the constant probing by the South American drug cartels. Europe was apparently several generations behind, hindered by the politics of power balance between the EU commission and the national governments. He suggested therefore that Europe was the better place for cleaning money. All that during his interview! Because there was a problem to solve, I hired him on the spot. Bright kid!"

"Why are you telling me this?" I managed to squeeze out. Despite all my worries, this was not a topic that I wanted to discuss with Tigran.

He laughed and said reassuringly, "Oh, Professor, relax. This is not one of those if-I-tell-you-I-must-kill-you things. I know you've had concerns about the source of my money and I am explaining it. Part of baring my soul to you..."

I was not sure that I wanted him to bare his soul, but I remained quiet. One cannot really stop a man from telling you what is on his mind—especially not a man like Tigran.

"So, contrary to my initial intent, and with some urging from Stiglitz, Mak'Ur, and, in fact, everything else that I have in the US is one hundred percent clean. America was to be the safe haven for me and my family, a place we could come when we were ready. You know, a clean start. And a kind of insurance policy..."

I was not sure how to react to this, so I just nodded dumbly. But I was certainly glad to learn that my concerns were unfounded, and that we were clean. Still...

"Anyway," he pressed on in a monotone, "I look at our

partnership as an understanding primarily between you and me—the two 'adults.' You brought Aram and I brought Stiglitz, and as I said, I have full confidence in the boys. If anyone can do what I ask, they can. Don't you agree?"

"They *are* a dynamic duo. But what you ask is huge," I muttered.

"On the other hand," he went on in the same vein, "I am not so sure about you, Professor. I know that what I ask of you is difficult. And I know that I am pushing—probably too hard. My apologies. But this is important for me and I want to explain why."

He shrugged and smiled, and as incongruous as an apology was with his normal demeanor, he tried to make it look genuine.

"Yes, Professor, you do worry me. I have no doubt that you are the best if not the only person who can solve the cost run rate problem. You call it a yield problem, but to me it is all about the cost. And, no, it is not a matter of technical talent. I know you have plenty. In addition, I could buy other technologists who could do more or less the same technical things that you do. But this is also a public relations problem. To the rest of the world, you *are* the front man for Mak'Ur. You personify its credibility. There is no one who can sell its clean bill of health like you can. And that is not something that I can buy in the time that I have. So, Professor, I depend on you."

I stared at him, not quite sure where he was going with this. On one hand he was complimentary, but on the other hand…

"The problem, Professor, is that you are thinking linearly. So, as per the spirit of our original agreement, I have come here to explain the situation so that you can understand why it is important that you make this problem go away—quickly—by any means possible. I suspect that you are one of those people who need to see a problem in its global context before starting to think outside the box." He made air quotes for emphases and added, "I like that term: thinking outside the box; it is so descriptive. And so American! So, am I right? Do you need to see the whole picture before you can focus on a specific detail?"

I might have shrugged at this. I knew that debug takes time for good and understandable reasons, and was confident that it was not a matter of lack of some global vision on my part, or of my motivation, or to whatever else he might attribute my reticence; rather it was a simple cold hard truth, whether he liked it or not. On the other hand, the tone of the conversation was making me nervous. I was in the cross hairs and understood that this was not necessarily the best time to argue. So I said nothing.

He eyed me pointedly and continued. "I assume that I am right, Professor. I want to share some information, and I trust that you will respect it as confidential."

I could hardly tell him that I hate having to keep secrets, or that I did not want to know too much about him because I suspected that I would find something dirty. It would not be an appropriate thing to say for a partner who had taken an oath at the outset of our shared commitment.

"Well, Professor, it is like this: During the past twenty to thirty years I have worked very hard to build my business. I have accumulated interests in the wine and cognac trade. Also mining enterprises, as well as agricultural concerns... And, shall we say, service businesses. The aggregate works well, with the individual lines of business meshing nicely—cogs in a proverbial machine—which makes the whole integrated conglomerate more valuable than the sum of the pieces. Except for my interests in America—those, as I said, I keep separate."

He took another sip of the brandy, and then let out a deep sigh. Perhaps he was feeling some hesitation about his decision to reveal what still lay hidden.

"The pandemic has been very rough on this business machine," he continued. "I am facing a situation for which I had not planned. I was unprepared and am now risking a total unravelling of the conglomerate. This is not only bad for me and for my family, but for all the people that have come to depend on my enterprises. The way the conglomerate is set up, it is an all-or-nothing situation. It is not as if I can sacrifice a part of the enterprise to save costs. Except for the American operation. So, I am faced with a fundamental choice: either I save the conglomerate by selling my American interests, including Mak'Ur, or I allow the conglomerate to unravel, and run. The problem right now is that there are still too many loose ends for me to drop out; so, in a way, I have no choice. I have to sell Mak'Ur in order to protect my family and the conglomerate. Do you see?"

"Not really," I responded honestly. My argumentative side was awakening. "I certainly do not mean to tell you your business, but I think I understand that you need to inject some money into your European operations because of the pandemic. But can't you go to the banks to secure a bridge loan? Everybody else seems to be doing so. Would that not be a better move than a fire sale of your US investments? Especially while we are dealing with the cost run rate problem?"

"Well," he responded with a bit of a smirk, "on the surface that would seem the obvious course of action, but it is not that simple. To explain fully I must go back to the dark '90s. Because in our part of the world doesn't everything go back to the '90s?"

He hemmed and hawed a bit, and then said that what he was about to tell me would have to be just between the two of us and re-emphasized that he would trust me to keep it that way. And before I even had a chance to protest, he went on to explain how, in the wake of the collapse of the Soviet empire, he managed to take over several different enterprises.

"Then two big things happened," he said. He stopped there and sat in silence for a long time, perhaps reliving that period. Then he shook his head as if to bring himself back to the here and now, and continued. "On one hand, I had a number of women approach me asking for my assistance to transport them to the west. You must understand that those were hard times. When the Soviet system collapsed and hyperinflation set in, entire families were left with no income, no savings, no job prospects, no safety net. Everything that we had grown up with—the entire system—unraveled. Perhaps the fact that some women saw no other option than to go to the west to sell their bodies best describes how hard it really was. These were not just druggy trollops off the streets. Some of these women had families and were highly educated with university degrees. Good women caught in a very hard spot... Having to do the best that they could with whatever assets they had. I knew, and they knew, that this meant prostitution. But they were desperate. They had to feed their families.

"So I helped not only to smuggle them across the borders, but also to set them up with contacts in the west. The one good thing about being Armenian is that we, like the Jews, have connections everywhere in the world. Mine were mostly through the wine and cognac trade. Some I even inherited from my father—mostly third or fourth generation Armenians living in France and England. So I used those connections..."

I remained quiet. I mean, I knew about the hard times and the women. During that time the running joke in what was left of Yugoslavia was that the fall of communism had really fucked the Russians—literally—because most of the prostitutes in Serbia at the time were Russian. And there was—and still is—significant press about girls from Moldova and Belarus, and other such sad places. But what was I to say to Tigran who was confessing that he had a hand in that? I saw it as disgusting, while he, on the other hand, did not seem to feel like it was anything to be ashamed of.

"After a while," he continued, "I realized that there was a real opportunity there. Smuggling these women across the borders and setting them up in the west to offer 'escort and entertainment' services turned out to be a very good business."

He made air quotes around 'escort and entertainment' services. Talk about giving a fancy name to a dirty business—and I did suspect that for him it really was just business. He refilled our snifters.

"This was not tawdry white slavery with girls walking the streets or skulking in dark corners. Nor was it anything like the fancy legal bordellos in red light areas. No, we catered to the high end—very rich men. These were sophisticated women offering high end entertainment and escort services. Sometimes companionship or even psychoanalysis! Not just sex. They were more like the Geishas in Japan, or the courtesans of the old European courts, before the uptight Victorian morality took over."

Probably feeling that further explanation of the business was necessary, he proceeded to elaborate.

"If you are catering to men who are willing to spend, say $50,000 or $100,000 for a watch, how much do you think they would be willing to spend for special entertainment experiences?

If this was, say, $10,000 for a special night (not that much by their standards), and if you managed, say, just thirty-three percent occupancy, and, say 100 women, you could have a business that turned over more than 100 million a year!"

He paused there to let the numbers burrow into my mind. I had no idea, of course. This was a totally alien world to me. One hundred thousand dollars for a watch?

"So," he pressed on, "it was much more about setting up the right business processes than just running girls. Creating the right environment. Making the right contacts. Recruiting and honing the right talents. Providing safety and security. Guaranteeing discretion. Manufacturing the right profile for these women and creating appropriate legends. Housing them. Establishing suitable channels for the flow of the money. It was not like this kind of clientele would leave the cash on the bedside table like in the movies.

"Altogether, it was a matter of setting up the right infrastructure for a luxury services and entertainment business... And, once we went up the learning curve, it turned out to be an excellent business for me. And for the ladies, too!"

He fell silent. All I heard was that he was a coyote smuggling people across borders and a glorified pimp running women for some rich men in Europe. The way I saw it, how rich his clients were did not make a difference. He obviously picked up on this, and proceeded to try to educate me.

"Catering to the needs and wants of rich people is the oldest profession and possibly best business in the world. It is a huge industry. We are talking hundreds of *billions* of dollars per year. In fact, last year just the so-called personal luxury goods market—fancy clothes, accessories, watches, jewelry—was worth about 300 billion dollars! That is excluding art, cars, travel and entertainment. That is comparable to the entire semiconductor industry—which, ironically, is probably the youngest business in the world. And it has better profit margins than those of the high-tech industry, requires less capital investment and carries lower risks. Rich people have the money and are willing to spend it if you offer them something they want. Trickle down really does work. And it has worked for millennia."

I was totally amazed. "Really?" I spluttered. The chip industry (in my biased opinion the highest exponent of human intellect and hence the pinnacle of the evolution of our species) had had an aggregate revenue of around 400 billion dollars during the past year. "Really?" I repeated. "So you are telling me that with all of our advanced education, highly specialized knowledge, mind-blowing technology, and ten-billion-dollar fabs, the chips that power the entire modern world generate only twenty-five percent more money than guys making overpriced handbags and fancy suits?" I was floored.

"Believe it," he nodded. "It is because your industry is run by boy-engineers who are more excited about showing off what they can do than about making money—as opposed to real businessmen who would know how to extract indisputable value…"

"Amazing!" was all I could muster as a response.

"So, if the rich are willing to spend 300 billion on fancy clothes and trinkets, how much do you think they spend on *services*? And how much do you think are they willing to spend on the special kinds of entertainment that we offer? Say, to be conservative, one to ten percent of what they spend on personal goods? That, Professor, is a three to thirty billion dollar a year opportunity! And that is the market in which I am involved…"

I began to understand the attraction that a margin hunting businessman would have for luxury 'services,' to use his name for it, and how any moral misgivings could be set aside. If everyone was willing—which for that kind of money, no doubt, everyone was—could consenting adults be faulted?

Satisfied that he'd made his point, Tigran continued his story.

"The other thing that was happening around that time—the collapse of the Soviet empire—was that there was basically a free-for-all competition for profitable businesses. The '90s were a lawless time in what used to be the Soviet Union. Have you ever read *McMafia*? No? Well, the one point that the book makes that I know is correct is that the collapse of a repressive system, accompanied with the zeal to set up new open democratic societies, has put a whole lot of the enforcement apparatus on the street. The secret police organizations of the Soviet empire—KGB, Stasi, ZOMO, Securitate, UDBA, NKVD—were suddenly unemployed and out on the streets with no income. So what were they to do? People skilled in setting up secret networks and extorting cooperation? They did what they were good at: organized, muscled their way into a number of lucrative companies, and moved into whatever operations would generate the cash that they needed to keep them in the style to which they were accustomed. Since the rest of the economy at the time was collapsing, they were naturally attracted to smuggling, arms trade, drugs, girls... Those not only matched their skill-set but, you see, illegal activities do tend to have some very attractive cash flows."

I was stunned, not so much by the revelation itself, since this matched what took place in Yugoslavia during the sanctions—basically, mafia running the place. I was much more surprised by him sharing the reality of his business with me.

"So," he continued, "we started rubbing against the operations of some of these syndicates. They saw what we were doing and thought that they would like to muscle in."

I was extremely uncomfortable. This was not something I wanted to know or discuss with *him*.

"Fortunately," he persisted, "I knew some of them—some Russians from the Soviet days. It was quite dicey for a while, but in the end I managed to convince them that our businesses in fact had nothing in common with each other. Theirs was about the numbers of girls, managing discipline and driving away the competition, whereas mine was about the infrastructure—like building bicycles versus crafting a Rolls Royce. Both have wheels, but... So, we reached an accommodation."

To me, of course, this was so distant from my own life experiences, and so abstract, that it seemed to be straight out of the movies.

"It was the only way that I could keep us safe," he carried on, now eager to explain. "These were ruthless, brutal people. Anyway, we made a deal to coexist. They agreed to stay out of the *luxury* escort and entertainment services. At the time, this line of business did not have the kind of volume that was required to buy and keep the loyalty of ten thousand unemployed ex-secret policemen. So they moved in on the retail end of the girl business and left me alone. In return I agreed to subcontract the security operations to them. This arrangement gave me access to muscle if and when I needed it, and kept all the other organized syndicates at bay. The Albanians... The Corsicans... More recently the Yakuza and the Triad... Everybody has appropriate respect for my Russian friends, so they leave my business alone. And in return I pay ten percent of my revenue for security and 'protection' services." He made the air quotes to stress protection. "About once a year we get together to renegotiate the protection fees, the political coverage favors, and other shared interests. You could call it extortion, but so far it had worked out and everybody was happy."

"Political coverage? What do you mean?" I asked, genuinely curious, and steering clear of 'extortion.'

"You see, Professor, luxury entertainment connects one with political elites. Politicians often use the services that we offer, and over the years I built up a network of connections in political circles which could be very useful for someone skating on the outer edges of the law. So I agreed to provide my Russian colleagues with political coverage if and when they needed it. That was a part of our bargain. A very important part because—unlike the protection money—this was something that they could not acquire elsewhere or replace. It was my trump card, and my insurance that they would stick to our agreement. Mind you, this too was high end. My connections were not used to protect their foot soldiers, only some of their chiefs, or their chiefs' stupid kids who got themselves into some kind of trouble."

It all sounded like stuff out of *The Godfather*—rival clans complaining that the Corleones were not sharing their judges... Wow! But that was fiction set in the 1940s, and Tigran was talking about reality in the twenty-first century!

"Since then," Tigran carried on, "the luxury service business has actually blossomed. We branched out into adjacent and more mainstream markets. Individual escorts, parties, business entertainment, medium and long term contracts, independent contractors... Men, women, straight, gay—whatever... And we went international...beyond Europe. Middle East, Japan, recently China... Not America, though... But always high end—expensive, exclusive, discrete. A very good business with very good margins, to the point that 'services' became the heart of my conglomerate. Other operations—the wines, the mines, and so on—are ongoing because they complement the service business. They provide some of the legitimate revenues and suitable channels for managing the cash flow of the entire enterprise. On the other hand, the service business provides protection for those other operations. One side cannot be sustained without the other. It is a balanced machine generating ten-digit revenues every year."

I was speechless. What could a mere silicon technologist who works for his living possibly add to that? Ten digits? That was more than a billion dollars a year!

"This arrangement has lasted for the past twenty years," Tigran embellished, presumably satisfied with my stumped reaction. "But then the damned pandemic came. The pandemic has really hurt the 'service' business. Understandably so, I guess. Not so much on the very high end, but certainly so on the side of business that contributed volume. People stopped travelling. People stayed at home with their wives. Parties and social get-togethers were cancelled. No escorts for fine dining. No physical contact entertainment business. In every geography our operation ground to a trickle." He paused there as if lamenting his misfortune.

"However, my counterparts are still there," he emphasized, "and they still want their protection fee. We have not finalized this year's numbers, but there has never been a time when my payment went down. Even back in 2009, during the financial crises, the best that I could do was to negotiate a flat year-on-year fee. I expect that it will be similar this time. They don't care that rich men do not want entertainment during the pandemic. All they want is their money."

He refilled our glasses.

"So, Professor, you tell me: Can I really go to the banks and ask them for a loan to pay off my so-called friends in the Russian mafia? Long story short, Professor, I need 100 to 150 million dollars to pay for the continued protection. So I have to sell my share of Mak'Ur and I need Mak'Ur to be valued at about a billion dollars... Or else...I am dead, and my business will be picked apart."

At that moment—before digesting and ruminating over the entire story—I actually felt sorry for Tigran. The way he told it, he appeared to be an innocent victim, just a businessman trying to survive.

"So, Professor, I trust that now you see why I need you to make the yield problem go away. By any means whatsoever..."

I knew I had to say something, but what? I certainly had no wise advice for a billionaire who needed to pay $100 million dollars in protection money. "Believe me," I postured, "solving the yield problem is not a question of extra motivation or extra work. If it were, then it would have already been solved. Believe me, the entire team is working full bore. These things take time because the entitlement duration of a full cycle of learning is on the order of a few months..."

"I understand that, Professor," he said, almost consoling me. "Clearly, I have nothing to contribute there. I believe you. Which is why I keep suggesting that perhaps you can make it *look* like the problem is solved," again emphasizing 'look.' "Which is different than actually solving the problem."

"In an industry that cannot keep a secret," I protested. "In an industry populated by pedantic engineers who like to measure everything, and who take pride in finding a typo on the forty-fifth page of a contract full of small print? Doubtful!"

"Well," he mused, "my friends in secret services tell me that misdirection is always easier than concealment. Apparently, when you have something that you do not want the other side to know about, it is easier to generate misinformation than it is to keep that one bit secret. Confuse the opponent. Manufacture bogus stories to keep him busy and distracted. Like in the spy movies. You do not send one mole to the enemy camp; you send in one mole and ten decoys! Is there not something along those lines that could be done?"

This was not something that I—even by furthest stretch of imagination—had ever thought about. 'Confusing the opponent' has never been proposed as an objective... Well, sure, sometimes certain things are kept quiet—such as trade secrets—but that was different. I did not understand the concept of misinformation in our domain. I don't know if he took my silence as a sign of concurrence or encouragement.

"They also tell me that misdirection is an art form that can be applied in different ways other than simply generating a lot of noise. Let me tell you a story that an associate of mine once shared with me. Back in the '90s he invested in a shipyard that had a contract to build navy ships, high-speed patrol boats for Iran, or Cuba or someone. Both parties were under the US sanctions, so they were more or less forced to work together. Apparently, ship building is a bit of an art and the performance of the product is just an estimate until after the first prototype is tested. So, they built this boat and were shocked to find that it did not meet the specified speed requirement. They were really in trouble as they had used up the money and the time that the contract allowed, and they had a boat that failed to meet the spec... So what do you think they did when their clients came for the initial acceptance tests? Their solution was brilliant in its simplicity: they simply moved the mile-markers used to measure the speed of the boat a bit closer together. You see, this was before GPS. Back then the speed of a boat was assessed by measuring the time taken between mile markers. So, they focused all the attention on the accuracy of the stop watches, statistical errors in timing, synchronization of different measurements, and everything else other than the distance between the mile markers. After all, who in their right mind would, under those circumstances, think about verifying the actual length of a kilometer. A brilliant example of misdirection! It apparently worked for them and the customers happily signed off on the contract and even ordered several more boats... Could something like that be done?"

I just shook my head in disbelief. The entire psychological construct was alien to me. Tigran looked at his watch, and said, "I am sorry, Professor. I did not realize the time. Please, excuse me."

At that moment one of those random spurious thoughts popped up in my mind: How much was that watch that he just looked at worth?

He rose, collected the half empty bottle and the glasses and said," Okay, Professor, I will leave it in your hands. Please, make the problem go away... Quickly... Or else I will have to..."

We exchanged hurried good-nights, and he left.

The rest of that trip was a blur. We stayed another half-day, flew back on the same jet, and were home before the weekend.

A Solution?

I do not know if it was Tigran's intent, but the things he said that night were like a virus that began to spread through my psyche. Indeed, if that was his plan, then he truly was a mind-manipulating super mutant reminiscent of *The Mule* in Asimov's Foundation Trilogy. Either way, in one sense Tigran was right: the only way that the yield problem could be fixed in the time frame that he was talking about was to cheat. To make it *look* like the problem was not there.

According to standard industry practices, even if we were to find the bug that very day, and we defined a revision that fixed it the next day, then we would still need a couple of months to build the new material to demonstrate the effectiveness of the revision, and depending on the nature of the fix, possibly an additional couple of months to qualify the revision and demonstrate that it did not affect product reliability. In reality, I suspected that it would take us a few more months just to identify the root cause of the bug and another month or so to define the fix.

If we were going to follow industry standard practices...

The only way to beat that schedule would be to change the specification limits to which the products were tested, and thus relabel failed parts as passing parts. You see, in general, few failures are of the kind where an IC is just broken and not working at all. Those kinds of fails are typically caused by design mistakes or by gross manufacturing defects. Those kinds of failures often produce what is lovingly referred to as a 'smoking hole' when a chip is powered up—an area on the chip that has self-destructed due to overheating. Those kinds of fails are usually easily identified, and the source is normally fixed very early on in product life cycle. This was not the case with our failures. No, most of our failures were random and often of the parametric type—the kind of failure that could be erased by changing the spec limits. Allow a larger current, or a lower voltage, or a slower response time, and a fail could be turned into a pass. That would make the problem seem to disappear.

Moving the spec limits would be the IC-equivalent of moving the mileposts just like in Tigran's story: in short, cheating. It worried me that Tigran seemed to have gotten into my head, and that I was actually considering doing such a thing. I knew that there were hundreds of spec limits that a 'good' IC was supposed to meet, as well as many places within the test procedures that offered opportunities to tweak the pass/fail criteria. There were many more opportunities to cheat than simply moving the mileposts.

In fact, modern ICs, and especially multichip modules like we were building, are complete systems, and determining which units are 'good' or 'bad' is an extremely complicated procedure. ICs are so complex that it is nearly impossible to directly test correct operation of a chip, and trying to demonstrate full functionality of each and every product unit would take an infinite amount of time. For example, if you were testing an adder— probably one of the simpler digital logic functions—just because you demonstrated that it correctly added two plus two to make four does not definitively prove that it would correctly add two plus three. A comprehensive direct functional test would require that all possible combinations of inputs and outputs were tested and verified, which would be a lengthy task. Thus, a fully functional test of an adder that only adds, say, two ten-digit binary numbers would require verification of about three hundred thousand combinations! And with the complexity of modern ICs which include a billion of such logic functions, there would be countless possible combinations, and functional testing would be an infinite (and impossible) task.

No, correct functionality of a given IC is verified on a small sample of units through a complex set of design verification procedures—bench tests, system tests, software tests, and the like—which, literally, take many months. Once a design is verified, an IC is assumed to be 'correct-by-construction' and the electrical tests performed on production units are done mostly just to demonstrate that they are free of manufacturing defects.

As with cars, specifications such as 0 to 60 mph acceleration time, or miles-per-gallon statistics, or even basic things like correct operation of all the buttons and switches, are demonstrated on a few sample prototypes, and not on each and every car that is sold. That would be silly, not to mention expensive.

Thus, Final Test—the last evaluation and the ultimate gate to shipping parts to a customer—is not used to demonstrate the correct functionality of a given IC. It is more complicated than that. Final Test uses multi-million-dollar specialized testing machines in combination with all sorts of design tricks and shortcuts to demonstrate that the IC is mostly free of defects. This relies on a series of self-test features, where special logic is designed into the chip in order to evaluate correct responsiveness of many sub-circuits.

Direct electrical measurements are performed only to ensure the compliance of a small number of circuits especially designed to be 'observable', and of the characteristics of output pins, with specific Pass/Fail criteria. A Pass is ultimately defined as seeing so many millivolts or so many microamps in so many nanoseconds on that sub-set of pins for given input conditions... These criteria are often dictated by industry standards, to insure that different chips manufactured by different vendors can 'talk' to each other. In addition some Pass/Fail criteria are defined to guarantee operation across a specified use range, again as an industry standard practice. For example, it would be prohibitively expensive to test all the units at all temperatures under which they are supposed to operate. So, based on extensive characterization and modeling, the spec limits at a given test temperature are tweaked to ensure adequate margins to allow for operation in, say, very cold Alaska as well as in very hot Death Valley. Or in an enclosed box versus in a water-cooled server... Similar margins are normally added to warranty operation over the entire allowed voltage range to account for, say, use of a new versus an old battery, clock frequency range, manufacturing process variability range, and so forth. Thus, some of the spec limits only insure the safety margins—the so called guard bands—to guarantee performance only under some extreme conditions, and have no bearing on operation in typical use conditions.

So, the software programs which operate and control the test equipment that ultimately sorts out the good versus the bad ICs actually offer many places where the specification limits could be changed, thereby changing the yield. Yes, just like moving the mileposts, except that the situation for ICs is far more convoluted—maybe more like the 'VW Dieselgate' ploy where sneaky manipulation of the software allowed it to *look* like its cars were meeting the regulatory emission requirements. Nevertheless, in principle it was still the same kind of cheating as moving the mileposts.

Right at the start of our yield bust nightmare we'd categorized the observed failure modes, and around two thirds of the excess failures we saw were in fact of the type that could be recovered by a spec change. If we were to recover those fails, it would bring our average yield to somewhere around seventy percent. Not quite what we expected but a lot better than the wild oscillations between zero percent and eighty percent that we were experiencing. We could live with an average seventy percent yield. We could even make money with a consistent seventy percent yield. We certainly could declare victory and say that there was no problem, or if there ever had been a problem, that it was now fixed...

However, changing the specification limit is complicated, and not something that could be done on a whim, even if that whim came from a corporate CTO.

Standard industry practice is that any change in specification requires a signoff by the clients. Clients normally perform an incoming test on a sample of the units that they receive, and a supplier cannot move his spec limits without moving the customers' ones at the same time. And for that a client's concurrence and signoff is required. Normally, depending on the proposed change, this signoff could be a simple paper exercise where they review and concur with the change, or it could be a demand for a full requalification that would require new data, and maybe even a repeat of the reliability tests. Or they could just refuse a change and threaten to go with a competitor...

I knew that in order to get the clients' concurrence and signoff, we would need them to focus on something innocuous, rather than on a change that might impact important product attributes. I had to put something in front of them that they were likely to accept as a paper exercise, not something like product guard bands, which would normally be considered too risky. It was a well-accepted axiom in the industry that reducing design margins was a going-out-of-business strategy, and changing product guard bands could potentially have very dire consequences in the market. There are few things that frustrate a customer as much as a brand-new appliance that worked perfectly well in the shop but does not work when it is plugged in at home because maybe it was a hot day; or maybe the range was wired on the same circuit as the new appliance, or whatever. Those were the kind of failure modes that could be precipitated by reduced design margins. Hence, guard bands were something that no one dared to touch. In fact, they are so deeply ingrained in all standard practices that I believed that the original rationale behind them have been forgotten and lost in the mists of time. It was just known rule: *thou shalt not mess with the guard bands and margins...*

So I would need to pretend that there was no change to those specs. What was it that Tigran had called it? Misdirection...

I hatched a plan.

I suspected that at least a part of the problem causing our yield issues was something to do with mechanical stresses caused by material mismatches resulting in an ever-so-slight warping of our chips. Silicon, the base material used in making the ICs, is quite stiff and brittle, but under the right circumstances, such as when it is thinned down, it can actually warp. Here we are talking about warpage that is far less than the width of a human hair, but even so, when a chip warps, device characteristics can change.

Normally, this warpage of chips just does not happen. Normally, this mechanism is so esoteric that few semiconductor technologists are even aware of it; maybe something that they learned about in school, but normally quickly forgotten in real life. In fact, the only reason that I, myself, thought of it was because this guy who I noticed only because of his Yugoslav-sounding last name was making noise about it. A few years ago he'd published several papers on the topic and had given a few talks at conferences. That, and the fact that the modules with the yield problem were rectangular rather than square, which probably resulted in asymmetric distribution of mechanical stresses, made me think of this warpage mechanism. I was pretty sure that the chip warpage issue did not explain the whole of our yield problem, but I thought that it might be a contributing factor. We would know for sure in maybe two months, once the material with the experiments intended to address that possibility came out of the pipeline.

But the failure mechanism was possible and sufficiently esoteric for my scheme. I planned to put in a Process Change Notice that would require the chips to be made slightly thicker than they were in the current modules, supposedly to minimize the warpage. Making the die thicker is an innocuous enough change. With normal digital ICs everything happens on the surface layer that is just a few nanometers thick, so that whether the die is two hundred or three hundred micrometers thick would not matter. I expected that most of our clients would readily sign off on such a change.

Along with this proposed change in die thickness I planned to release a new test program with relaxed specs. I would not tell our clients about these, since I was pretty sure that they would not readily sign off on a spec change that affected the guard bands. I hoped and prayed that no one would notice the change to spec limit numbers buried deep within the test program, and that everyone would instead focus on looking at the thicker die and what this might mean to the product.

Misdirection...

Yes, I knew that this was cheating. Yes, I knew that this was a dishonest, slight-of-hand trickery. Yes, I knew that this was not the kind of a thing that a professional in our industry would ever consider. Yes, I knew that there were some risks to our products, and worse, that we would be shipping modules that might precipitate problems for some of our clients' products.

Yes, I knew that what I was thinking of doing was not only immoral but probably illegal. Yes, I knew that if this came out it could result in heavy fines (as it did for VW) and that ultimately it could lead to the failure of Mak'Ur. Yes, I knew that if discovered it would destroy my reputation. Yes, I knew that if found out I might even end up going to jail! All this I knew…

But I felt I had no choice.

It was not so that I would maximize the value of my share in Mak'Ur. No. Even if Mak'Ur was sold for half of that billion that Tigran wanted, I would be richer than I ever expected. I was not doing it for personal gain. It was because I was frightened. Tigran had made it clear. "*Make the problem go away quickly. Or else I will have to…*" Those words were seared into my mind. He might as well have said, "*Handle it or I will have my Russian mafia friends pay you a visit to encourage you…*" Or something along those lines…

I did not spend a lot of time mentally playing out the various scenarios that could actually take place if Tigran and his buddies were to get involved. What would this mean? Would they hurt me; or God forbid, hurt Bev or Lara? Would they simply get rid of me and find some other sucker to fill my role? I did not know and did not want to find out. What I did know was that I was frightened and felt I had no choice. I had to make the problem go away. Period.

Besides, the engineer in me—or maybe it was the gambler—whispered that the risk of being caught was low. Perhaps mostly to console my conscience, he whispered that the probability of anyone noticing the change to the guard band specs in the test program with millions of lines of code was minimal. That VW was caught cheating with its diesel engines only because there was a regulatory government body whose job was to look for that kind of a thing. There is nothing like that for ICs. And even then, VW got away with it for years… The whisperer said that the actual risk to our product in normal operating conditions was low, and that the probability of our products actually experiencing minus 40 C to plus 85 C temperatures, even if used in Alaska or in Death Valley, was low.

Either way, I had no choice.

THE REALITY

Well, it almost worked. Almost...

As expected, most of our clients approved the Process Change Notice. Some did it virtually overnight, and some took a week or two. Some had probably not even read the PCN, basically trusting that whatever the change it would be innocuous. Some had clearly read it all and were concerned enough to ask questions. As expected, they asked mostly about the reasons for a thicker die, and the impact that it might have on the thermal performance or on mechanical integrity tests. Some even wanted to talk about the Piezoelectric Effect!

I suspect that it helped to be a famous professor with whom most young engineers would not argue. Normally, PCN approvals are viewed as a kind of a bureaucratic hassle that is typically assigned to junior engineers in the Quality Assurance departments—those who would not have the confidence to question me. Usually, young engineers try to impress with how much they know and understand, and not by challenging a CTO. All easily dealt with, really... I even flew to San Jose so that I could field some of the questions in person.

Besides, I did not want to leave an email trail asking my test engineer to doctor the Pass/Fail criteria in the test program. Some things are better dealt with in person. The engineer that I had in mind for this delicate task happened to be based in San Jose, and I knew that he had personal issues that made him hungry for money. I believe he mentioned something about a wife with cancer, or something equally heartbreaking—enough motivation, I would think, to look the other way in order to maximize the value of the company and his stock option. Besides,

I was the CTO and he would simply be following orders... which I would need him to keep very quiet about for a few months only.

But then Elvira, aka Dr. Barbara Vasquez, called. She was certainly not someone who was intimidated by me.

We exchanged the usual updates on the phone, pretending—or play-acting—like we were friends, which we were not in our private lives. But we had met enough times to be quite familiar with each other—sort of professional friends. So our calls usually started with inquiries about families or our pastimes, some conversation about the progress of the respective companies, or maybe a bit of gossip about events in the industry. In the absence of anything else there was always the fallback exchange about the weather, since she typically spent most of her time in Los Angeles.

After a few minutes of this preliminary banter, she asked the killer question—the one that I was dreading. "Look, Professor, I understand that you have sent us a request for PCN approval..."

"Yes," I responded quickly—perhaps somewhat nervously—since PCN's rarely reach all the way up to the CEO of a company. "We have seen possible sensitivities in some of our products, and have determined that a thicker die is more robust," I explained hurriedly, using the standard response that had by that time been well polished.

"Yes, I saw that," she responded in her confident voice, "but," she carried on, "my engineers tell me that there has also been a change in some of the Pass/Fail criteria in the latest revision of your test program. Was that intentional?"

There it was; the question that I'd feared. And from Elvira, too, to make it worse!

"What?" I feigned confusion.

I had of course played out this scenario in my head, obviously hoping that it would not come up. If it did come up, my plan was to pretend to be confused, to deny any intentions of changing the specs, to claim that it must be some kind of a bureaucratic mistake, and to promise to look into it, and to fix it. What else could I do? Especially with a client like Elvira, Inc.

"Good," she allowed. "I suspected as much... I heard that

you are having some yield challenges, and I would not expect that you of all the people would try to navigate around those by sneaking in a spec change."

This was said in a matter-of-fact way, but she made it clear that she knew exactly what was going on, and that she was watching us carefully.

"No, no, of course not," I protested.

"Because," she inserted before I had a chance to add any more excuses, "I may be on your Board, but my first and primary loyalty is to my company. I do not have any conflict of interest when it comes to the quality of the material that we buy."

Well, that put me in my place. She'd made it clear that there was no wiggle room, and that she would not cut us any slack. In fact, she made it crystal clear that she would be watching us carefully. She probably had a source of information somewhere in our supply chain—seeing that she knew about the yield bust. We, of course, tried to keep as quiet as we could about that, but she clearly knew enough.

So, I really had no choice.

"Sorry, Barbara. I will look into it and fix it. My apologies," was all that I could say, hoping that I sounded more confident than I really felt at the moment. We hung up with the usual cordial exchange.

"You are so fucked!" was all that I could say to myself. And to the universe...

Now what?

In fact, I knew what I had to do. My subconscious must have been mulling the topic without me being fully aware of it. Perhaps I was even hoping that something like this would happen to give me a good excuse to abort what I was doing. I took the rest of the day to consider my options.

There were none.

I sent an email to Tigran, asking him to call me on a secure line because I had an update that he would want to know about. Ten hours later he did—at 3:00 o'clock am Pacific Standard Time.

"Speak," was all he said. No preliminaries. Not even hello. I presume that this was a direct translation of the Russian or

Armenian version of *kazi*, which was not an unusual way for busy people to answer a phone in Serbia.

I explained everything to him while trying to be as succinct and non-technical as I could. He listened.

"This is Barbara Vasquez, the woman on the Mak'Ur Board of Directors?" he asked, presumably to make sure.

I confirmed, and after a short silence he came back with the words that made me break into cold sweat. "Okay, Professor, thanks for telling me. You did the right thing. Leave it with me now. My colleagues will need a week or so. I will let you know when it is safe for you to talk to her again."

I sensed that he was about to hang up, so I hurriedly yelled, "Wait!" My imperative was met with silence. "I do not want your security services anywhere near her. I really could not live with myself if anything were to happen to Barbara. Please stay out of this!" I blurted before I'd really had a chance to think it through.

To this day I am not sure I know why I reacted that way. All I know is that I could not possibly condone the kind of activities that I associated with the Russian mafia anywhere near the world which I associated with Elvira. I did not even have a clear picture of what those 'activities' might be. Maybe it had to do with the way the movies presented the Russians nowadays. When I was a kid the Russians were usually portrayed as bumbling spies, or maybe as some kind of incompetent bureaucrats dressed in baggy drab colored suits. Harmless and somewhat lovable. Nowadays the Russians are portrayed as brutal people covered in all sorts of special tattoos and doing things so unthinkable that the cameras usually pan away.

Just before I said 'hello' to make sure that he was still on the line, he asked in his usual calm and steady voice, "Do you have some alternative plan in mind?"

"Well, no... Maybe... I don't know... Let me think about it... I need time. Please stay out of this."

Upon reflection it was obvious even to me that it would not take a rocket scientist to figure out that the way I sounded made it clear that in fact I had nothing, that I was only delaying things. And, for sure, someone who I only recently equated to The Mule from the Foundation Trilogy would know instantly that I was just fishing…

"Don't worry, Professor," Tigran responded, "these are real professionals. They will know what to do. Trust me."

This time I was silent.

"Look," he added, "when we got involved in the past things worked out quite well for you, didn't they?" he said, presumably still trying to reassure me.

"You got involved in the past?" I asked, puzzled by what he meant. "How? When?"

"Well yes, of course," he laughed. "But not so much. You did not need much help. Have you forgotten your Round-A investors? I helped to secure the funding, didn't I? And that *New York Times* reporter—what was his name…Mike Eesahag—it just took a little incentive to encourage him to write that article. No rough stuff was needed. That was good, was it not? And Nakasone-san? He required some encouragement too—just a few nice girls—to provide you with the chiplets you needed during the pandemic turbulence. That was helpful, was it not?"

I was dumbfounded. I'd had no idea…

"Look," he continued, "in general the rich and powerful tend to respond to carrots a lot better than to sticks. There need not be any violence. They typically have big egos and do not take kindly to being pushed around. They think that they are too strong or too smart and above persuasion of that kind. So, some reasoning, or some incentives may be all that is required." He carried on, presumably still thinking that this was reassuring to me: "Violence works best on the oppressed masses, to use a phrase from *Das Kapital*. They are easily intimidated and easily frightened. My security detail is quite good and they will do the right thing. Don't worry, Professor. It will depend on how Ms. Vasquez reacts."

But something in me rebelled. Something that was dormant seemed to have awakened. Before I thought it through, I let it slip out. "No! No, Tigran, I do not want your goons anywhere near Barbara. Leave her alone!"

He remained silent.

"Believe me, if anything happens to her, I will go public. I will let the police know. Do you hear me? Stay away from her!"

I am not sure why I said that. It was not as if Elvira were some 'little woman' who triggered a male protective instinct within me. *Au contraire...* She exuded competence and confidence and made it clear that she could take care of herself. I think it was intuitive. Perhaps I wanted, or needed, to keep what I felt were shameful facts my association with the shady world of an Armenian Oligarch and his Russian Mafia goons secret from her. And Tigran was proposing to make that connection.

Dead silence filled the line, giving me time to realize what it was that I'd just said. My mouth was clearly working faster than my brain. "Oh, shit," was all that I could say, but to myself, inwardly. Had I just threatened Tigran? "Oh, shit!"

"Professor," Tigran came back, calm and cool. "I wish you had not said that..." After a pause during which I died a thousand times, he carried on, "Look, I will pretend that I did not hear that..."

Then there was an ominous pause.

"As I explained to you in Cyprus, I need you to sell Mak'Ur's clean bill of health. But, make no mistake, Professor, if I have to, I will proceed without you. I will not allow you to make difficulties... I must cash out and I must collect 100 million. That is not optional for me, so I will do what I have to do—even if it means replacing you. Do you understand? It is a business imperative, not personal." Steady. Cool. Calm. No inflection or intonation. No nothing. Just a cold hard statement of facts.

I, on the other hand, came close to wetting myself. I mean, it was the middle of the night, I was in bed, and I might have had a tiny accident. I was very frightened but glad that I was taking this call alone in San Jose rather than at home with Bev next to me. Explaining it to her would have been impossible.

"Goddamn, shit and fuck!" Inwardly, of course; to Tigran I said nothing.

I mean, what can one say to an oligarch who just assured you that he would eliminate you if you got in his way? In tones like he was just asking you to pass the salt, please... Clearly he was a man who had dealt with this kind of situation before. "All right, Professor, good night," he said and hung up.

"Now what, genius?" I said aloud to the empty room.

THE PLAN

What was I thinking? Even if he was only an Armenian oligarch, this one had *friends* in the Russian Mafia.

I did not go back to sleep that night. It took me hours to calm down enough to stop tossing and turning. A part of me wanted to run and hide. But there was no hiding from the graphic scenarios that were playing in my head. My imagination was clearly out of control. Maybe I had seen too many murder dramas on TV. Or maybe I had heard too many stories from friends and family about mafia killings in Yugoslavia. I might have buried my head underneath my pillow.

But hiding was not really an option, of course. I had to decide what to do, and to accept that whatever I chose would have consequences, even if I chose to do nothing.

My rational side wanted to construct some kind of decision matrix that would intelligently determine the right thing to do. If I could only calm down enough and think reasonably... Surely, there was a smart way out of this mess, I bolstered myself. Surely, it was only the drama queen in me that was conjuring up frightening pictures. Calm down, I told myself.

So, what was it that he wanted me to do...or not do? Go public? All right... I won't, I swear. I will not say anything to anyone. And I would even manufacture the legend about the disappearance of any and all yield problems as Tigran had suggested.

Truth be told, I knew that in the end I would say anything, do anything, or cover-up anything if it meant sheltering my family. Family comes first. And they can do whatever the hell they want to Elvira. It was so stupid of me to pick a fight with Tigran over his goons approaching Elvira.

After a while—perhaps only after I'd had a shower and brunch and called in to take the day off—a certain clarity began to emerge. I put myself in Tigran's shoes and realized that I had managed to make myself a liability for him. After all, it was I who had opened the door to the idea of going public and revealing *things*... In fact, it occurred to me, it was possible that my fate was sealed that night in Cyprus when Tigran told me all those things. I may have become a liability by simply knowing what I knew about him, let alone threatening him about going public!

From the beginning Tigran had said that he could be quite vindictive with people who disappointed him. I now saw this trait of his in an entirely new light. If Tigran was really as ruthless as I thought Russian mafia was, then I was a dead man.

If I refused to cooperate and did not help him sell Mak'Ur, he would move me out of the way. Sooner rather than later. First, so that I could not obstruct him; secondly so as to leave no loose ends. He'd all but said so. Maybe also to get even with a disobedient and awkward ex-partner who had disappointed him... End result, I was dead.

On the other hand, if I did cooperate and helped him drum up the value of Mak'Ur, and even if we did sell it for that one billion that he wanted, he would most likely still decide to move me out of the way. I reasoned that he might not do anything about the liability that I had become in the short term because he needed me; but three months, six months down the road, after Mak'Ur was sold, he would want to close the gap. Surely, a thoughtful, cautious man like Tigran, in a precarious position, would not leave loose ends. And for him, I was a loose end...

Furthermore, it was clear to me that if someone really did acquire Mak'Ur, it would not take them long to realize that there was a cost problem, and that there had been a cover-up. There would be an inquiry... Like that HP-Autonomy acquisition. Trials. Convictions. Fines. Public shame. Maybe even jail time...

And then Tigran would need a scapegoat. Dead people are the best scapegoats. They cannot fight back or leak compromising information. Easiest for everybody involved to say that they had no idea about cost issues, yield problems, or whatever.

Easiest to blame the CTO who was in charge at the time. Easiest for everyone if that CTO was not around to contradict them or to say anything awkward...

The next question that popped into my mind was inevitable: is there anything at all that I could do to impact the unpleasant outcome that I now foresaw? My first instinct was to run to the police or to someone in authority. Maybe that was the adult version of running to mommy for help? After all, I was only trying to stop a fraudulent act: the sale of Mak'Ur under false pretenses. And a potentially violent act: the murder of Yours Truly. Surely they would protect me. I was the good guy here.

It took only a few seconds to realize that this was stupid and useless. If anyone had committed an illegal act so far, it was me in trying to move the test specs. Stupid, stupid me! And Tigran? Clearly there was absolutely nothing on him. If I did go to the police, they would most likely dismiss me as a paranoid lunatic; certainly they could do nothing. No, all that going to the police would accomplish was to alert Tigran that I had become something more than a loose end.

So, what if I hired a bodyguard to protect me? Private police? I questioned, not ready to give up. Further thought convinced me that this would most likely be ineffective since I could not hope to win an arms race against the Russian mafia. Or outlast them in a waiting game...

Altogether it became painfully clear to me that if Tigran and his Russian 'security services' wanted me gone, I would be gone. Sooner or later, no matter what I did. If they wanted me dead, I could not stop them. The only way to stay alive was to make sure that they did not want me dead.

So, if I wanted to stay alive, I had to carry on trying to bury the yield issues. To carry on doing my best to perpetuate the lie, and hide the cost overruns. To do exactly what Tigran wanted, and be useful to him and to help implement his scheme. Manufacture a legend and assure the world that everything was copasetic. That there were no issues... I realized that the only thing keeping me alive was the perpetuation of that lie, which was quite a sobering thought.

And afterward? I questioned myself. After Mak'Ur was sold

and I was needed as a scapegoat, how would I stop them then? A conundrum. My helping them now would only assure my demise later.

Perhaps... A ray of hope shone somewhere in my head. Perhaps there was a way of finding a very narrow, twisting, path between these two scenarios. Perhaps... I scrambled to hold on to that notion.

What if I was to manufacture and sell that legend all the way up to the end game, and then did an about-face and revealed the truth just before the deal closed? Become a whistleblower at the eleventh hour? That would keep me alive up to that eleventh hour, as far as Tigran and his goons were concerned, and protect me afterward from the subsequent investigation by the buyers, or the state, or whomever...

But that would not protect me from Tigran's vindictiveness...

So, what if I gave Tigran my share of Mak'Ur? A thought. A hope... What if I made sure that he got his $100 million, regardless of the Mak'Ur sale price? That was his objective and, being a rational man, he should not care how he got to it. Fifteen percent of a billion-dollar company should be the same to him as thirty percent of a half-billion-dollar company.

A plan was beginning to emerge. If I kept myself alive by collaborating as long as possible, and then became a whistleblower at the last possible moment, then under those circumstances Tigran would have no options but to accept my offer as a *fait-accompli*? He would not have time to find a new buyer for Mak'Ur, and so he would have no choice but to accept the sub-one-billion offer on the table and take my share. Basically, that would be buying my life with my share of Mak'ur.

Good trade off IMHO, I encouraged myself. I may not end up with any money but... Who needs money? Staying alive was so much better.

Yes, that might work. As long as Tigran kept his vindictiveness in check and did not decide to eliminate me out of spite. Or after he collected the money...

I only hoped that he would be rational, and that getting rid of me afterward would not be worth the hassle. As a whistleblower I would have some visibility, and maybe that would protect me.

Maybe I could even get some kind of witness protection.

Of course I wavered as I played out the extreme scenarios in my head. One minute I was berating myself for being such a drama queen, sure in my conviction that I was just imagining most of the threats and that surely, surely Tigran was not a murderer; and even if he was, it would not be in his interest to have me killed, and that after all, this was America and twenty-first century, and that these kinds of things just did not happen...

And ten minutes later I was equally convinced that I was a goner no matter what I did, and that the only option that I might have was to pick the how, and maybe the when. I was a wreck.

Over time I convinced myself that I could either drive myself crazy fretting and worrying, or I could maintain my sanity by resolving to accept the plan of action and to keep myself busy executing it. Perhaps an act of faith, but in fact, I decided, the only path open to me.

First I set up a daily call with Aram and Stiglitz to keep an eye on the activities associated with the sale of the company, not so much because I wanted to be in the loop and to know exactly what was going on, but because it would give me some insight into how much time I had. I had to be ready for my 'eleventh hour.' Exact timing was important to the plan.

Stiglitz and I also worked out a system for reporting the cost overheads associated with the yield bust. I knew that we were playing accounting games to obscure the real cost issues (I guess we both knew this but had mutually decided to not talk about it). I also knew that this was illegal but thought that it would not matter once I *blew the whistle*. I mean, there are laws that protect whistleblowers, aren't there?

Secondly, as per those movie scenes when a doctor tells someone that he has only a few months to live, I decided to 'put my affairs in order.' I found a suitable lawyer in San Jose and set up a trust fund with Bev and Lara as the sole beneficiaries. I placed all my Mak'Ur shares in it. I prepared a will...just in case. And I wrote a letter to Bev to explain things. That was hard and took a couple of days of writing and rewriting, but I had to tell her that I loved her, to thank her for being part of my life, and that I was sorry. And to give her an explanation of the events that would have led to my end. I gave three copies of this letter to the lawyer with instructions to mail them if something happened to me—to our home address and to her office address—in case someone decided to intercept her mail. And one to be hand delivered before the reading of the will.

Of course, there was a part of me that wanted to hop on a plane and run back home to Bev to unburden myself, to tell her everything, to hug and seek comfort in her embrace. But I also knew that this would only summon worries that she could do nothing about. She would probably rebel against an unacceptable situation. She would rant and rave, maybe even put on her passionate civil rights lawyer robe and righteously insist that we should fight for what was right and fair and just. As if there were some legal injunction that a judge could sign that would keep the Russian mafia away. I knew Bev. She would believe that there was something that could be done to affect the outcome. I knew that this was naïve. Perhaps that was the remnant of the fatalistic Yugoslav in me versus her optimistic Americanism. I knew that if we did go down that path all we would achieve was to put her in danger too. Maybe Lara as well. And probably hasten my end. No, Bev was not the type of person who would just eat the worry and stay out of it.

Better that I stay away, I steeled myself. It is the right thing to do. After all, it is my mess and I have to clean it up all by myself. Leave Bev out of it. The plan I have is the best thing to do, I assured myself. Anyway, if everything worked out the way I hoped it would, then my staying on the West Coast would be just another absence, and that letter would never see the light of day. It would be moot and irrelevant.

Thirdly, I wrote a letter to Elvira. I swallowed my pride and confessed, explained everything to her. I apologized for the cheap shot of the spec change, and most importantly warned her about the possible visit to her by Tigran's 'security services.' I outlined the situation, admitted to my complicity, and gave her a thumb sketch of my plan of action. I assured her that my whistleblowing would trump any cover-up that she may or may not take part in, freely or under duress. So, I urged her that, if and when a visit by the Russians occurred, she should agree to whatever they asked her to do in order to keep safe. My whistleblowing would make her statements moot, and she would not be guilty of complicity in a cover-up.

In the greater scheme of things, what Elvira did or said would not make much difference, so she might as well do whatever would keep her whole and safe. Given my plan, whatever she did or said was not much more than a delay tactic.

After some vacillation I decided to send the letter in hard form, on paper by regular mail. I thought that paper mail would be more secure than electronic mail. In this day and age and with Russians involved I thought that it was more likely that they would be sniffing my computer than intercepting paper mail. A funny image of a circus bear dressed in a tux and a top hat riding a unicycle popped into my mind (probably due to all the stuff in the recent news about 'Fancy Bear'—a name that NSA had given to Russian hackers). Yes, I would use USPS and drop the letter into a mailbox on some street corner, or even at a post office. They would never know.

Then I wrote a quick technical paper to be published in the next issue of *IEEE Electronic Transactions Letters*. I guess my name, my reputation and my connections made it possible for me to jump the normal queues, skip the reviews, and get my paper published just a few weeks after submission. The paper described some of our yield problems and proposed that these were due entirely to stress interactions. It also claimed that all the yield losses were totally eliminated by use of slightly thicker die.

A lot of this was bogus, of course, but I thought it was possible and credible, especially since I cherry-picked the data and the observations to match the theory. It would pass a cursory-read test by a non-expert, but would fail a thorough examination of someone in the know—especially if complete data were to be presented. Definitely an inglorious milestone in my career.

Of course, where I come from—academia—this was the worst sin possible. Falsifying data! Not only highly immoral but illegal. Like that Elizabeth Homes lady and her Theranos start-up. Or that Han-dude from Iowa State. I knew that what I was doing was a sin that would earn me a prominent place on that wall-of-shame of people caught falsifying data—people who were outed, shamed, and sometimes even jailed for doing exactly what I was doing. I knew all that, but…

I did it to manufacture a 'legend,' to use Tigran's word, which would quash any rumors that might have leaked out about our yield problems. What was it that he'd said? The best way to obfuscate was to misinform rather than to hide… And, yes, Tigran was right, and given my name and my reputation, I could do that more effectively than anyone else. That was why he kept me around. I did it to make Tigran feel that I was a good boy and doing what he'd told me to do. And, presumably, to keep myself alive…

Next, I wrote a short report that documented the real story of our yield bust, and that described the real cost and yield numbers. It also described the accounting tricks that Stiglitz and I had put in place to hide the reality, and presumably to mislead the potential auditors and/or buyers. The whistleblowing report was only a couple of pages long. Funny how truth can be expressed so succinctly, whereas lies require a lot of words.

I made two copies of the report. I printed it, photographed the pages, and destroyed the original, thinking that photographs of text would be harder to locate with the computer search algorithms than regular text files. One copy was intended for whoever would be acting as the lead in buying Mak'Ur. The plan was that I would send them this at the eleventh hour when I was ready to blow the whistle. And one copy was for a journalist acquaintance; he was a freelance writer who often contributed to industry rags like *EE Times*, *Semiconductor Engineering*, *DigiTimes* and others. Over the years I have interacted with him and we occasionally met on the conference circuit and caught up over coffee or lunch. I liked him and trusted that he would know what to do with the report that I'd written.

I would e-mail these when the time was right. A click of the button and the deed would be done. Until then, I simply encoded and saved the jpeg files.

Finally, I wrote a short letter to Tigran explaining the reason for my eleventh-hour news release. I thought that coming clean might be the best way to approach him and insisted that my actions were in the best long-term interest of *all* the partners. I debated with myself whether I should point out that if anything were to happen to me, then the authorities would naturally follow the money and scrutinize all the Mak'Ur stakeholders. I was obviously banking that this scrutiny would be bad for him and hoping to convince him that getting even with me would not be worth the risk. But I decided that Tigran would figure that out all by himself. And finally, I explained that I felt responsible for Mak'Ur not reaching the one-billion-dollar valuation that he needed and made him an offer of enough of my shares to complete his 100 million gain. It all seemed reasonable to me, as well as a no-lose proposition for him.

I searched my memory and realized that from the very beginning all communications with Tigran had always been oral and face to face. Phone or email had been used only to coordinate those meetings. I decided that given that, it was possible that someone was watching *him*, and that therefore he would appreciate it if a potentially incriminating letter like the one I'd just written was not sent as an e-mail or through the regular postal services. Maybe that consideration would help to get me on his good side.

Altogether I spent a lot of time thinking through this aspect of my plan, mostly because I was concerned that it would be really unfortunate if at the critical time after my whistleblowing he were to make a rash decision and order my death just because my letter did not get to him in time —like those ironic scenes in the movies. Seeing that my life might depend on it, I thought it was worth spending the time to consider every aspect and possibility, and the money to make sure the letter reached him within twenty-four hours. So I looked online and found a private international courier service who would hand carry a letter to anywhere on the planet and guarantee delivery within twenty-four hours. For a fee, of course. I prepaid for the courier and arranged for a printed copy to be hand delivered to three places: Tigran's address in Armenia, his address in Cyprus, and to a third address to be phoned in later—just in case I found out at the last minute that Tigran was somewhere else. To be delivered when I decided to *pull the trigger*.

I also decided that witness protection for me and my

family—if it came to that—would have to be negotiated once everything was out in the open. Trying to bring it up now would only complicate an already convoluted issue, and might precipitate concerns about my motives and my honesty.

And finally, I booked an open ticket for a flight that would get me to Kotor in Montenegro. San Francisco to Frankfurt, Frankfurt to Dubrovnik. For two reasons.

First and foremost, I thought that if and when that eleventh hour came, and I did blow the proverbial whistle, it would be safest if I were somewhere out of sight, somewhere unreachable. Far away from Bev and Lara—just to make sure that they would not end up as collateral damage. At least until everybody was fully informed and had had a chance to cool down. So I thought I would hide in my personal version of that hole-in-the-wall that Butch Cassidy and Sundance Kid kept: my family home in Kotor, Montenegro. I felt safe there.

The second reason was that if I were going to end up dead, it might as well be there—the place where we used to visit our grandparents during summer holidays when we were kids. A happy place.

And just to be neat and tidy, I erased all potentially incriminating letters or files from my computer. Cleanliness is next to godliness.

All the elements were primed and ready for me to pull the trigger when the moment was right. I just needed to keep my fingers on the pulse of the company and wait for that proverbial 'eleventh hour.' Timing was of the essence. It was important that the whistleblowing report, the letter to Tigran and my 'disappearance' coincided. My life might depend on it.

Finally, all that was left to do was to write a full account of the entire saga. My complete explanation for Bev and Lara. My full whistleblower report. I would bring it with me to Kotor and finish it there. Then I would hide it in a nook where Bev would know to look for it. Of course, if things went to plan, no one would ever see this complete account.

It would be only words in the wind.

EPILOGUE

- *THE POST-GAZETTE* -

OBITUARIES   October 31, 2020

It is with great sadness that we are announcing the passing of Dr. Andrija (Andrew) Krstić. He died from injuries sustained in a traffic accident in Kotor, Montenegro, sometime after 3:00pm local time (CET), on October 30th, 2020.

Andrija Krstić was born in Belgrade, Yugoslavia, (now Serbia) on October 17th, 1961. A single son to Vladimir and Dusanka Krstić, he grew up and was schooled there until 1985, when he earned his first degree in Electronic Engineering from University of Belgrade. He won the Nikola Tesla Scholarship and completed his PhD studies at the Bessemer-Morgan University (BMU) in 1991. He stayed at BMU as a member of the academic staff of the School of Electrical and Computer Engineering and has held the Alfred S. Harris endowed chair since 2001. He authored and/or co-authored 23 books and over 425 technical papers and has received multiple awards for best papers published in industry leading journals and conference proceedings. Dr. Krstić was a recipient of the SRC Inventor Recognition Award and was elected an IEEE Fellow in 2003. He was the Editor of IEEE Transactions on Device Technology between 2003 and 2010, and served in multiple roles for ICCAD, ISSCC and DAC conferences. He left his academic career at BMU to serve as Chief Technology Officer at Mak'Ur AI Inc.,—a company that he cofounded in 2016 with one of his students, Dr. Aram Khachaturian.

He is survived by his spouse Beverly Krstić (nee Bernard) of 26 years, and daughter Lara Krstić. No words can possibly express the grief for their loss of a loving husband, friend and companion, and of a father and a 'guidelight.'

Dr Andrija Krstić has inspired many and will be missed by all his friends and colleagues, including the staff at BMU, his many undergraduate, graduate and postgraduate students, and fellow professionals who were fortunate enough to have collaborated with 'the professor.'

Services will be held at 10 a.m., Wednesday, Nov. 10, at the McCall Funeral Home Chapel of Memories. Burial will be in the Union Cemetery. Friends may call at the McCall Funeral Home from 9 a.m. to 7 p.m., Tuesday Nov. 9. The family will receive friends from 6 to 7 p.m., Tuesday Nov. 9, at the funeral home.

Semiconductor Technology & Industry Quidnunc

Clark Kent   Dec 18, 2020

Chimera Merges with Mak'Ur AI to Position itself in the Smart-Home Sector

Chimera Fund, a brand new SPAC that has been formed just a few weeks ago, has merged with Mak'Ur AI Inc., a privately held company that completed its Round-B funding only about a year ago. The smart-home segment of the AI market is clearly experiencing rapid consolidation—probably in preparation for the growth rates forecast to be between 25% and 30% CAGR in the 2022 to 2025 period. Although the unexpected announcement of the merger came only last week, the deal must have been planned months ago—well ahead of Chimera's IPO, and the recent unfortunate demise of Dr Andrew Krstic, Mak'Ur's co-founder and CTO.

According to sources, the transaction was estimated to be worth around $1 billion, involving cash and stock swap—the highest valued deal so far in the smart-home sector.

The official merger date is scheduled for March 26th, 2021, subject to regulatory approval. Given that Chimera is just a newly formed SPAC with no pre-existing position in the market, no issues are expected.

Chimera has been launched in early October as a 'blank cheque company' focused on carving out a dominant position in the nascent sector at the intersection of Artificial Intelligence technology and the consumer market. It was funded to the tune of $2.7 billion, with a known industry luminary Dr. Moustapha Makh at its helm, and with Elon Umingmak and Andrew Jaune on its Technology Board. Clearly this is a company that is moving very rapidly, intent on becoming a powerhouse in the Consumer Artificial Intelligence market—a sector which is yet to be fully defined but which is expected to experience explosive growth over the next decade.

Mak'Ur AI Inc was co-founded in 2016 by prof. Andrew Krstic and Dr Aram Khachaturian of BMU, focused on custom AI software and hardware solutions for the smart-home market. It raised $56M in Round-A funding in 2017, and $150M in Round-B in 2019. Its interconnect standards, software and hardware solutions focused on realizing an integrated smart-home have apparently been very well received by the established players in the home appliance and private systems integration markets.

Dr Aram Khachaturian is expected to continue as the EVP in charge of a smart-home subsidiary of Chimera Fund.

Dr Barbara Vasquez, CEO of Home Security Systems, and a member of Mak'Ur AI BoD has stated that the two companies have been collaborating for years, and that the Mak'Ur AI software and hardware products are now fully integrated in the HSS top of the line systems. "Mak'Ur AI solutions have come to the market at the right time, with capabilities that enable us to offer our home and office customers unparalleled levels of security, with revolutionary user-friendly features, and at a price level that is a game-changer in the security market. We are very excited about the opportunities that the Chimera acquisition opens up. It will provide Mak'Ur AI with the capital required to fuel the expected expansion of this sector."

ACKNOWLEDGMENTS

This is the third book in a series of fictional stories placed in the high-tech world of the semiconductor industry. After thirty-five-odd years as an engineer, and a mere three years as a writer, the author has eagerly sought encouragement and feedback from family, friends and. all comments were appreciated, and any and all honest feedback were priceless for much more than just the editorial value. To all of those who have had the patience: Thank you.

The author was especially touched by the support, effort, comments and suggestions from:

- ✓ Matt Nowak and Taravat Khadivi (aka TeraWatti) who have been volunteered to be 'in-situ readers' and who have worked their way through the manuscript as it was being written, and have offered some awesome feedback. Thank you.

- ✓ Natasha (aka #1) Radojcic and Lara Llosa, who have so many more things to do in their lives, and plenty of better books to read, but have chosen to work their way through the manuscript and give Dad good feedback. Thank you.

- ✓ Dan Perry, Vesna Niketic and Dejan Radojcic, who have read the initial, unedited, and unpolished version of the completed manuscript and provided some very insightful comments. Thank you.

- ✓ Orthocoronavirinae, more commonly recognized as Coronavirus 2 (aka SARS-CoV-2), responsible for the coronavirus disease of 2019 (aka COVID-19), for keeping the author properly locked-up and duly undistracted for long enough to finish the story in record time—and even to do so much more...

✓ David Ross and the team at Open Books, for giving this book a chance, for having the patience to edit it into what it is now, and for educating the author about what it is like to work with a real professional team. Thank you

Thank you one and all! This book would not be what it is without you.

ABOUT THE AUTHOR

Riko Radojcic is a lucky man who has been blessed with a fulfilling life rich in its diversity. He was born in what was then a poor post-war Yugoslavia and enjoyed a very happy and secure early childhood there. When he was twelve his father took a job with the UN World Health Organization, and Riko spent his teen years in East Pakistan (Bangladesh now), Nigeria, Kenya and Tanzania, observing both the demise of the colonial Raj, and some harsh Third World realities. He completed high school in Swiss private schools—a polar opposite of the Third World—which gave him a peek into the lives of the one-percenters. He then moved to Manchester, UK, where he witnessed the bleak circumstances of the working class in the heart of the then-decaying industrial England. He earned his BSc and PhD degrees in Electronic Engineering and Solid-State Physics there, and after a couple of years of working in England he immigrated to the US. Riko and his then-wife settled in the San Diego area, where they brought up their three wonderful children, and he got to experience the American Dream—yet another polar opposite. He enjoyed a rewarding and a very stimulating career in the semiconductor industry, working in a variety of technical, managerial and business development roles. His professional life exposed him not only to the amazing wonders of the silicon chip technology, but also gave him an opportunity to travel internationally and to interact with smart and talented people from very diverse and multicultural backgrounds. After thirty-five-plus years in the world of high tech and engineering management, Riko retired and is now a writer. Always more comfortable as an observer than the observed, as an analyst than a participant, he is trying to bring to life the magic of technology, the reality of the high-tech industry, and some of his diverse life experiences through storytelling.

Other books by the Author:

FICTION			
Between the Dragons	Fulton Books	2021	ISBN: 978-1637100622
Between the Titans	Fulton Books	2020	ISBN: 978-1646541775
MANAGMENT			
Managing More-than-Moore Integration Technology Development	Springer	2018	ISBN: 978-3-319-92700-8
TECHNICAL			
More-than-Moore 2.5D and 3D SiP Integration	Springer	2017	ISBN: 978-3-319-52547-1
Stress Management for 3D ICS Using Through Silicon Vias	American Inst. of Physics (AIP)	2012	ISBN: 978-0735409385
Three Dimensional System Integration	Springer	2011	ISBN: 978-1-4419-0961-9
Guidebook for Managing Silicon Chip Reliability	CRC Press	1999	ISBN: 978-0367400064

Made in the USA
Las Vegas, NV
10 April 2022

47185003R10121